LOVE **is** FOR **ever**

Also by Jean Ure
for Younger Readers

Woodside School Stories
The Fright
King of Spuds
Loud Mouth
Soppy Birthday
Who's for the Zoo?
Who's Talking?

LOVE **is** FOR **ever**

jean **URE**

ORCHARD BOOKS
96 Leonard Street, London EC2A 4RH
Orchard Books Australia
14 Mars Road, Lane Cove, NSW 2066
ISBN 1 86039 770 0 (A format paperback)
First published in Great Britain 1996
First paperback publication 1996
This edition first published in 1998

A CIP catalogue record for this book is available from the British Library.
Printed in Great Britain

chapter **one**

Grown-ups don't believe you can be in love when you're only thirteen. Not properly in love. My mum calls it calf love, meaning that it's something you grow out of, like puppy fat or spots. When I tell her that love is *for ever*, she just laughs and says, "For ever is a mighty long time!"

I once heard her talking to my nan when they didn't know I was there. Well, actually, to be honest, I just had this feeling that they were going to talk about me and so I hung around and listened. I don't see why I shouldn't have. People oughtn't to discuss you behind your back. Anyway, I heard Mum say, "She's got this boy-friend, Paul. They're in the same class at school and they go everywhere together. One of our neighbours said she saw them walking down the street the other day, holding hands."

Yes, and I know who *that* was. That was old Nosy Parker Gullick. Her that lives next door. She's always spying on me.

So Nan makes this little cooing noise and says, "I think that's rather sweet."

Yeeeeuuuurgh! It isn't *sweet*. It's hormones, as a matter of fact. We did it in PSE. Hormones make you attracted to members of the opposite sex (usually). Paul and I once went all round Rackhams (which is a big posh department store for anyone who hasn't heard of it) holding hands and chanting, "It's our *hor*mones, it's our *hor*mones!" All the respectable middle-aged ladies that do their shopping in there kept giving us these really sour looks. Paul said they were just jealous because they'd probably forgotten all about hormones. I said, "If they ever had any," and that made us giggle and we started picking out all the ones that might have done and all the ones that almost certainly never had.

"*She* didn't. *She* didn't. She might have done!"

In the end they asked us to leave. I expect you can understand it, really. The middle-aged ladies were getting quite hot and cross. Maybe it was bad manners but it was kind of funny, trying to imagine them with hormones.

But to go back to Mum and Nan. When Nan said she thought it was sweet, Mum said, "Yes, I suppose. In a way. But she's far too young for this sort of thing!"

I don't know what she meant by "this sort of thing". If she meant love, then I don't think that you are ever too young. (You might be too *old*. People seem to become terribly sour and embittered as they grow old, very often.) If, on the other hand, she meant hormones, then she obviously doesn't know very much about human biology. Perhaps they didn't do it – biology, I mean – when she was a girl. They were very old-fashioned in those days.

I remember Nan said, "I'm sure it's all perfectly innocent" and Mum said, "It's not that I'm bothered about. But she shouldn't be tying herself down like this! She ought to have girlfriends, and be going around in a gang."

What cheek! I do have girlfriends, as Mum knows perfectly well. I have Esther, who lives in the flat upstairs, and Carina, who is in my class. Ess is my *best* friend, but unfortunately we don't go to the same school. Carrie is my *school* friend. I don't go round in a gang because I don't happen to like gangs. I like to be on my own with either

Paul or Ess, or maybe Carrie. Mum only keeps on about gangs because when she was at school she used to belong to one called the Wally Mob (after their leader, whose name was Susan Walters). She is always telling me about the Wally Mob and the things they got up to.

It occurs to me that if Mum was still messing about with the Wally Mob when she was thirteen, she must have been incredibly young for her age.

Nan stuck up for me a bit. She said, "Tracey's the independent sort. She's a mind of her own." (I'm glad Nan thinks this!) "She likely wouldn't be happy in a crowd."

Mum said, "No, but where's it going to lead to? How is she going to get on with her school-work and pass her exams if she's mooning about over some boy?"

And then Nan said something which completely destroyed all the happy glow I'd got from her sticking up for me and telling Mum that I had a mind of my own. She said, "I shouldn't worry too much, if I were you. She'll be long over it by the time she sits her GSCs, or whatever they are." (Nan can never keep up with what's happening in school.) "This time next year she'll be wondering what she ever saw in him."

Well, that is just where Nan is wrong! Just as wrong as wrong can be. No matter what happens, I will always love Paul. Even if I never see him again – even if he hates me and won't talk to me any more – it won't stop me loving him. Except that if he rejects me, I am not at all sure that I will be able to go on living. Then perhaps Mum will realize that what she calls calf love is just as serious and everlasting as any other kind.

But it will be too late then.

I still can't believe all that has happened. It is like a sort of nightmare that just goes on and on. It's hard to look back and remember that only a short while ago I was happy and untroubled. The only worry I had was a spot on my chin. Should I squeeze it or should I not? Pathetic!

The spot has gone away, but the nightmare continues. If I were Paul, I don't know that I would ever forgive me.

I am sitting in my bedroom writing this because I have got to do *something*. I can't just mope, which is what I would do if not otherwise occupied. I can't go up and commune with Ess, because she's been taken off to her nan's for half-term; and Carrie, I happen to know, has her cousin staying with her and besides, we never really see each other out of school. Mum and Squirrel have gone into town shopping.

Squirrel is my brother. His real name is Cyril, but when he was tiny he couldn't pronounce it properly, he always called himself Squirrel, which is probably what he will always be. It suits him, anyway. He's nine years old and quite a nerdy sort of person. His hair grows to a point on top of his head, so that he looks like a turnip. He takes after Dad, who is long and thin and also a bit pointy. (But Dad is not a nerd. He is a bus driver and in Birmingham, I can tell you, bus drivers have to be *tough*. I don't think Squirrel will ever be able to be one. Anyone hassles him and he goes running straight to Mum.)

I am glad to say that when it comes to looks, I am more like Mum than like Dad. Mum is small and neat with a round face and bluey eyes and hair that is thick and honey-coloured. Everyone says I am the spitting image of her.

The only difference (apart from Mum's waistline, which she complains has *spread*) is that Mum's hair is short and mine is long. Mum says short hair suits the older woman. I once thought about having mine cut the same way, but then one day Paul told me that he thought long hair was r-r-r-romantic and so I changed my mind and kept it like it was.

I have to wear it in a ponytail for school, as they have these absurd rules about hair. It has to be "neat" and off the face and what Mr Smethurst, our head teacher, calls "conforming to normality". This means that a boy who tried coming into school one day with his hair dyed like a Union Jack, and all stuck up like a lavatory brush, was told to go away and not come back until he could conform to normality.

I think that is silly, as it is far more fun if everyone looks different, and what is wrong with Union-Jack-coloured hair? Carrie saw it and said that it was quite pretty. But I don't think I would like it if Paul's hair was dyed into stripes, as Paul's hair is very nice the way it is. It is very dark, almost black, with a bit in front that keeps falling into his eyes so that every now and again he has to flick it back. It kills me when he does that. It makes something churn in the pit of my stomach. It's like having butterflies fluttering in there. Lots of things about Paul make me have butterflies in my stomach.

For instance, when we hold hands or when

he kisses me. I have never been kissed by any other boy, except for Justin Slade in kindergarten. I don't ever want to be. There is a girl at school called Myra Carmirelli who thinks that this is pathetic. She claims that she has been kissed by practically every boy in the class. (But not by Paul!!!) She says, "If you just stick with the same guy all the time, you'll become dull and boring and fuddy-duddy. You'll become *middle-aged*."

I told this to Paul and he said a rude word which I'd better not write down in case someone ever sees this (though it is not meant for any eyes other than my own, except maybe Ess's. I shall have to think about that).

I suppose Paul does use bad language rather a lot. But not in a nasty way. He uses it as if it's normal everyday speech, like I might say, for instance, "Get lost!" if Squirrel is annoying me, which he does quite often, and Paul would say – well, I won't say what he would say, but it's something Mum and Dad would not approve of. It's stupid, really, because when I say "Get lost!" I sometimes say it in a really horrible, angry tone of voice, but when Paul says what he says, he does it in just a quite ordinary, friendly fashion, and yet

Mum and Dad would still complain more about his language than about mine.

Whenever they have films on television and there are four-letter words, they immediately switch off and won't let me watch. I think that is being over-protective. I would rather hear four-letter words than watch a dog being killed, which is what happened in one film I saw which was meant for *children*, for goodness' sake. I couldn't sleep at night for thinking about it, whereas a few four-letter words don't upset me.

Mum says people who swear are violent, but Paul isn't at all. In spite of bad language and living on the Digdon Estate, he is far more gentle than most of the other boys in our class. There are lots of them who tell filthy jokes and think girls are just rubbish, but Paul is not like that. He's even nice to Squirrel when I am nasty to him, and once when we had gone for a walk we found this pigeon that had been injured and Paul picked it up and put it in someone's back garden, under some bushes, so that it could either get better or at least die in peace and not be run over or stamped on. I bet there are some boys in our class that would have chucked stones at it. They are like that, some of them.

These are the ones that think it's soppy to go out with a girl. They used to take the mick out of Paul at first, but they don't any more. He's tough enough to beat them to a pulp if he had to, so now they respect him. He was a bit of a scrapper when we were in Year 7, he was always getting into fights and being hauled in to see Mr Smethurst. But he only ever fought boys who were as tough as he was; he never picked on weaker ones. Like he wouldn't ever hurt an animal or bash a kid. Once he even told me off for yelling at Squirrel that I would put poison in his food if he ever dared mess with my things again. Paul said that Squirrel was littler than me and that I was frightening him. I don't think I was, actually, but Paul won't ever let me bully him. That is one reason I *knew* he couldn't have done what they accused him of doing.

Then there was the other reason, of course.

Mum was ever so good about it, really. Lots of mothers would have walloped me, or at any rate yelled, but Mum didn't do either. On the other hand, I doubt if she'll let me stay behind when they go to Auntie Ellen's again.

It hardly seems possible it was only a week ago that it happened. I feel as if I've lived a lifetime.

Mum said to me that she and Dad and Squirrel were driving out to Hagley on Saturday afternoon to spend the day with Auntie Ellen and Uncle Jack, and did I want to go with them? She said, "You don't have to, if you don't want to. You're old enough now to make up your own mind."

So I said I'd rather not, because all they ever do, Mum and Dad and Auntie Ellen and Uncle Jack, is play endless games of cards and drink endless cups of tea and talk about boring grown-up relatives and the various illnesses that they have had. It's all right for Squirrel, because he can play with the twins (they are called Jason and Julie, they are eight years old and they are *repulsive*), but there isn't even a budgie or a goldfish for me to talk to. It's really dire.

Mum said it would be OK for me not to go so long as I promised faithfully to be back indoors by seven o'clock, "*No later*", and so long as I spent the evening upstairs with Ess. She said, "I don't want you in the flat by yourself."

Of course, I am writing all this from memory and so I cannot always write the *exact* words that people said, but that is definitely what Mum said: "I don't want you in the flat by yourself." She didn't say anything about being in the flat with someone else.

All the same, I knew that I was cheating her. I told her I'd ask Ess, but I didn't tell her *what* I was going to ask Ess. Ess is my best friend; she'll do anything for me. Even tell lies. I said, "If Mum ever says anything, will you say that I was up here with you?" Ess promised that she would. She thinks it's romantic, me and Paul being in love with each other. She hasn't got a boyfriend as she goes to this all-girls school, but she likes to read romantic novels and watch weepy movies on the TV, such as *Sleepless in Seattle*, which is her current number-one favourite. Afterwards she goes to bed and dreams that someone like Tom Hanks is kissing her. This is what she told me.

(In case there is anyone who lives on another planet and has never heard of Tom Hanks, like for instance a person who may discover this journal long after I am dead and gone, I will just say that he is a movie star who drives people like Ess into a delirium. Personally I prefer Tom Cruise, who is another movie star. But I would rather have Paul than either of them!)

Mum and Dad and Squirrel set off for Hagley

at two o'clock. Mum said, "Remember! You go up to Esther's. We'll be home about ten."

When they'd gone I went into town to meet Paul and we went to Cannon Hill Park, which is what we quite often do, and then afterwards we walked back into town and mooched around the shops for a bit and bumped into two of the kids from school, who told us we looked like an old married couple. They sniggered about this, but I didn't care and I don't think Paul did, either.

On the way home we stopped off at the supermarket and bought some Coke and a tin of baked beans, and a tin of peaches and a loaf of bread. I thought we'd better not use any of Mum's stuff in case she missed it and wondered where it had gone. I was supposed to be having tea with Ess.

It was fun going shopping with Paul. It was something we'd never done before; not food shopping, like real couples do. When we got home I made some toast and cooked the baked beans and Paul opened the peaches and we put everything on a tray and took it into the sitting room so that we could eat and watch the telly at the same time.

When we'd finished, I said I had to wash things up and put them away so that Mum wouldn't know they'd been used, so I did the washing and Paul wiped, because unlike Dad (who won't lift a finger) he is *not* a male chauvinist. Even though he is on the boxing team at school and was once called a "tough nut" by a supply teacher we had, he is not ashamed to do things which other boys might consider to be girls' stuff. For instance, he knows how to knit! This really surprised me when I discovered it. He said that he had learned to do it when his mum decided to try knitting baby clothes. His mum had never knitted before and she kept getting it all wrong and dropping stitches and not being able to cast on properly, so Paul had to help her.

I must say that when he told me this I thought that his mum must be a right useless kind of person. I cannot imagine a mother who doesn't know how to knit!!! I think this is really peculiar. I hadn't ever met Paul's mum when he told me about the knitting. Now I have and I was right. She is totally and utterly *useless*. But she is Paul's mum and I suppose he loves her.

After we'd done the washing up we went back to the sitting room and played some music, but not too loud in case Mrs Gullick, who is the Nosy Parker who lives next door, might hear it and complain to Mum. She is always complaining. Sometimes she bangs on the wall with her stick. I hate her.

Ess had lent me a video that she got for her birthday. It is called *Wuthering Heights*, which is a strange sort of title, but it comes from a very famous book by Emily Brontë that Ess simply adores. The video was extremely old, in black and white, and it was not what I would call a boy's video as it had rather a lot of love in it, being mainly about a man called Heathcliff and a woman called Cathy, who dies. However, Paul said he didn't mind as it put him in the right mood. I said, "Right mood for what?" and he grinned and said, "What do you think?" and I blushed and wished I hadn't asked.

It was the first time we had ever been on our own indoors before. Always in the past Mum or Dad had been there. (We never went to Paul's place. He never seemed to want to, and now I know why.)

I said, "Don't you go getting ideas," though I wouldn't really have minded if he had. Paul said, "I can't help it. It's my hormones," and he started tickling me, which made me go all goofy and silly, and we rolled about for a bit on the sofa in a way we couldn't do in front of other people. Then I said that we were meant to be watching Ess's video – "She'll want to know what I thought of it" – and I made him stop rolling about and sit up properly and behave himself.

We held hands while we watched the old *Wuthering Heights* thing. I didn't honestly think it was terribly good, but I decided I would tell Ess that I liked the man who played Heathcliff, who was someone called Laurence Olivier that I have never heard of, which is not very surprising as he must be quite ancient by now if not actually dead. I thought that that would please her, as I know she was turned on by him and that for a little while after she'd seen the film she dreamt about him instead of Tom Hanks.

While the video was rewinding I said, "Old married couple!" and giggled, but Paul said old married couples don't roll about on the sofa or sit and hold hands. He said, "I bet your mum and dad never do that," and I had to admit that they don't. So I said, "All right! *Young* married couple," thinking of Paul's mum and dad – well, his mum and stepdad. He didn't have a dad for years and then his mum found herself this new bloke and they got married, which was when we were in Juniors, Year 5. (We weren't an item, then. We were only ten years old; just dumb little kids. I didn't even like Paul very much. I thought he was a bit of a loudmouth and a show-off. He thought I was stuck up and snobby. It just goes to show that you can't always trust first appearances.)

I said, "If you were a *young* married couple you'd hold hands." "No, you wouldn't," said Paul. "You'd yell and scream and throw things." I said, "Why? What would you do that for?" Paul said, "Because you would." I said, "Is that what we'll do?" and he promised that it wasn't, because "We're different."

I would have liked to talk more about us being different, but just at that moment there was a knock at the front door and I froze and didn't know what to do, because of not being supposed to be there, but we went out and peered through the spyhole and it was Ess, so we let her in and she said, "Your mum just rang. It was a good thing I got to the phone before anyone else! I told her you were in the loo, so she said could I tell you they've been held up and won't be back till about eleven. Did you watch the video? Did you like it?"

So then we had to talk about the video and about Ess wishing she could meet a man like Heathcliff – which is odd, to say the least, considering Heathcliff was like a raving nutter and she *hates* macho men – and I really began to think she was never going to go, but in the end she got the message and went back upstairs to her own flat. I mean, Ess is really nice and my very *best* friend, but I wanted Paul and me to be on our own and keep on playing at being married.

Unfortunately, by this time it was nearly half-past ten and quite suddenly Paul announced that he had to go. I couldn't understand why, since Mum and Dad weren't going to be back for another half an hour at least and Paul's mum never cares what time he gets in. He stayed out all night once, after he'd had a row with his stepdad.

I don't know what the row was about; he wouldn't tell me. He just said they'd had one. I didn't try pushing him. I've learned when to shut up. But it must have been an absolutely mega row, I would have thought. I mean, to stay out *all night*. I can't ever imagine doing a thing like that.

When he came to school next day, he hadn't had any breakfast and his stomach started making these rumbling noises in the middle of maths and everyone laughed, but it wasn't really funny. His mum is *utterly* useless. Even when he's there she doesn't make him a proper breakfast, just a cup of tea and a bit of bread and jam. He's always hungry. I expect that's why he has what Carrie calls "a lean and wolfish look". It's because he isn't fed right.

I said if he waited I'd make him a cup of coffee, but he wouldn't. He said he'd got to go now, like immediately, and I thought it must be something I'd done or said, though I couldn't think what. It was only afterwards that I thought perhaps it was because I'd made us sit up straight and watch the video instead of rolling about on the sofa. I thought maybe he hadn't really wanted to watch the video, and I wished that I hadn't made him. I thought that I'd been bossy and that boys don't like that kind of thing.

As we walked along the passage to the lift I heard a click and knew that old Nosy Parker Gullick had opened her door and was spying on us. I felt like turning round and making a rude gesture, but I didn't dare in case she told Mum. I only hoped she wouldn't tell her anyway, though there wasn't any reason why she should. She didn't know I was supposed to be upstairs with Ess.

The flat seemed really spooky after Paul had gone. I plumped up the cushions on the sofa and made everything all neat and tidy, but I didn't like to turn the telly on for company in case it made the set get hot. I thought Dad might notice if he wanted to watch *Match of the Day*, or something.

I stood at the window looking out, and as soon as I saw Mum and Dad's car I left the flat and went rushing downstairs to the entrance. Mum was surprised to see me. I said, "I've been keeping a look-out for you. Ess was tired. She wanted to go to bed."

Mum said, "Yes, I'm sorry we're so late. Your Uncle Dave called round and we stayed longer than we should have. I hope you apologized to Esther's mum?"

I assured her that I had and for the first time I felt a pang of guilt. I'd never lied to Mum before – not a really big lie. But I know if I'd asked her whether Paul could come round she'd have said no. Deep down she doesn't really approve of Paul. She doesn't like where he lives, she says it's a sink and full of problem families. She also doesn't like the way he speaks – she says it's "rough" – and she doesn't like the clothes he wears. Once when he came round he had on a pair of jeans with rips in them, and Dad said, "Oh, I see you're wearing your knee-peepers!" Dad thought he was being *really* funny. I told him it was style, and he thought that was even funnier.

Mum didn't think it funny. She said afterwards that she thought it was "disgraceful his mother lets him go round like that".

It's hardly Paul's fault if he has a mother who is useless. I don't think you should judge people by their mothers. I said this to Mum but she said, "People may not be able to help their upbringing but it affects them whether they like it or not."

She'd never have let Paul come round and that is why I lied to her, though I do realize it is no excuse. I am not trying to make excuses; just telling it all as it happened.

If I were writing a book this would probably be a good place to stop and have a break between one chapter and the next, so that is what I shall do.

chapter **two**

I WORRIED sick all day Sunday. I just couldn't think of any reason Paul would want to go rushing off like he had, unless it was something I'd done to upset him. I kept remembering how I'd told him to sit up straight and watch the video. I could hear my voice, sounding just like Mrs Hitchins's when she gets mad at us in class because we're slumped over our desks instead of paying attention.

I'd only been joking – well, half joking, because I did think we *ought* to watch the video – but Paul can't stand being pushed around. People pushing him around was the reason he got into so many scrapes in Year 7, until the class bully boys discovered he could stick up for himself.

He once punched two of Clive Meldrum's teeth out for him. He got into a right row over that, though it wasn't his fault. Clive Meldrum had picked on him, telling him he was a no-hoper just because he lived on the Estate. I thought it was really mean of Mr Smethurst to bawl him out for that. Even if Paul didn't tell him what Clive had said, which knowing Paul he most probably wouldn't, Clive is still oceans bigger than he is. But Paul has a bad reputation.

Anyone does, that comes from the Estate. If you're quiet and weedy, like a girl in our class called Kylie Brown, they say you're a retard and "trash from the dump". If you're like Paul and fight back, then you get a name for being aggressive. I think it's really unfair. There isn't anything wrong with Kylie except that she's shy, and Paul isn't ever aggressive, only when he's picked on.

But still and all, he doesn't like being pushed around.

I couldn't phone him because he's not on the phone. He used to be, but then one time I rang him and I couldn't get through and when I tried the operator she said the line was no longer in use. I said there must be a mistake, but she insisted that there wasn't, and when I asked Dad what it meant, he said, "They've either done a bunk or they haven't paid their bill."

Well, I knew they hadn't done a bunk because Paul was still in school, so I thought probably they couldn't have paid their bill, only I never liked to mention it.

There are certain subjects that you can't talk about to people. Like with Carrie, for instance, it's the fact that her mum is a single parent. She's really sensitive about that and so I pretend I don't know. And with Ess, it's her glasses. She has to wear these ones with really thick lenses, pebble lenses, they're called. She's blind as a bat without them. But she hates having attention drawn to it as she thinks her glasses make her look ugly, which in point of fact they don't, although it is true she is not beautiful. So on the whole I try not to notice. It is only kind to protect people's sensibilities.

Paul doesn't like people thinking that he's poor. I can understand this; I expect if I were poor I wouldn't want people knowing about it. And especially I wouldn't want them feeling sorry for me. That is what Paul can't stand: people feeling sorry for him. Once when he came to school without any money (he said he'd forgotten it but I don't believe his mum gave him any) I offered to lend him some, but he wouldn't take it.

I suppose he knew he wouldn't be able to pay me back. So then I offered to share my lunch with him, but all he'd take was a few chips "to stop you getting fat". I'm not fat, not in the least bit, and I *know* that he was hungry.

I have been wondering if there is any subject that I am sensitive about and would rather people didn't mention. I can't think of any, so maybe I am quite well balanced. The only thing that gets me mad is when Mum or Dad, or Auntie Ellen or Uncle Jack, or any other grown-up, teases me about being in love with Paul and tries to make a joke of it. That's one of the reasons I don't like going to Hagley, because last time I went Uncle Jack said, "And how is young love today? Still deep in the throes of passion?" And although he didn't actually *say* "Ho ho ho" or "Nudge nudge wink wink", I could tell that that was what he was thinking.

It was so embarrassing, it made me squirm. Also, it is an act of vandalism, like taking an object of beauty, such as Mum's crystal vase that she keeps on the mantelshelf, and smashing it to pieces. Or tearing the petals off a rosebud, or smearing paint down a clean white dress. It ruins things.

So that was part of the reason I didn't want to go to Hagley; not just because of wanting to be with Paul.

As I couldn't ring him, I went upstairs to talk to Ess instead. Ess was sympathetic, like she always is. She couldn't think of any reason Paul should suddenly go racing back home but she said she didn't think he could have been mad at me or she would have noticed when she came down to give me Mum's message. She said, "Why don't we call round and see him?" And then very quickly she added, "Well, you could call round. I don't expect he'd want me there."

I had to explain that I couldn't because a) we were going over to King's Norton to have lunch with my nan and b) I didn't think Paul would like it if I suddenly turned up on the doorstep.

Ess said, "Why? Because he lives on the Estate?"

Ess refuses to believe that the Estate is as bad as people say it is. She doesn't really know anyone from it, except Paul, because the school she goes to only has posh kids from places like Edgbaston and Solihull, or kids like her who are so totally and utterly brilliant that they have won scholarships. Kids from the Estate don't win scholarships. It is not surprising, really. In Ess's flat, for instance, there are loads and loads and positively *loads* of books, and her mum and dad are constantly doing improving things such as taking her to museums and art galleries. (They take me sometimes, too, but unfortunately it hasn't improved me very much.) I shouldn't think, on the Estate, you'd ever find a book; not unless it was propping up a bed, or something.

I said this to Ess once and she said, "That's tarring everyone with the same brush!" (She tends to say this sort of thing.) She said, "It's not giving people a chance."

I wasn't sure what she meant by this. I pointed out that everyone *knew* the Estate was the pits, full of criminals and crack addicts and drop-outs, and she said, "What about Paul? Are you saying he's those things?" and I suddenly saw what she was getting at. Everyone thinks Paul is a tough nut just because of where he comes from. That is how he has got such a bad reputation. He has been tarred with the same brush as the others.

Ess said, "There could be hordes of people living there who've got really good brains and just haven't been given the chance to develop them."

Ess is ever so liberal; she never thinks badly of anyone. But in this case she was right. Paul, for example, has never been given a chance. I bet if he'd grown up with parents like Ess's he'd have won a scholarship to King Edward's. I just bet he would!

Usually, as a rule, I quite like going to my nan's. She has this roly-poly dog called Dish (short for Dish Mop) that I take for walks, and she always gives us something scrummy and squishy to eat before we go home, like cream horns filled to bursting or chocolate fudge all thick and gluggy. But I didn't enjoy it that Sunday, partly because of being worried about Paul, and partly because of beginning to have a really bad conscience about telling lies to Mum, and partly because Auntie Nonie and Uncle Frank were there and *they* started teasing me about Paul, saying really stupid things such as, "When is the wedding?" and, "Oh, look, she's blushing!"

Sometimes I think it is a great burden having so many relations and that it would be better to be like Paul and have none. It is true that you would not get presents at Christmas or on your birthday, but neither would you always be having to go on visits and listen as people made idiotic personal remarks and poked fun at your private emotional life. The worst is that you cannot even answer back, because then you are accused of being rude. As it was, Nan said, "What's the matter with our Trace today? Bit down in the dumps, is she?"

It made me want to gnash my teeth and foam. Instead I took Dish for a walk in the park and seethed quietly to myself, leaving Squirrel behind to be ever so sweet-little-boyish and make up for me having the hump. All I really wanted was for it to be tomorrow so that I could go to school and see Paul and check he wasn't mad at me.

He wasn't. I was so relieved! At break we went off by ourselves to one of our secret places. We have lots of secret places we go to. Carrie knows about them but she is the only one – I hope! – and she never comes prying. It's just that we like sometimes to be on our own.

As soon as we were away from the maddening crowd Paul said, "Were you all right Saturday after I'd gone?" He said he'd felt bad about leaving me but he'd suddenly remembered something. He didn't say what it was that he'd remembered and I didn't like to ask, because I've learned that sometimes with Paul there are things he's not going to tell and that is that. If you try pushing him, he clams up and goes all dark and moody. So I just said that I'd been OK and that Mum and Dad had arrived back quite soon.

And then there was a silence, which wouldn't usually have bothered me because when you love someone you don't have to keep talking all the time as you do with other people (though I don't with Ess) but on this occasion it was strange and awkward, and I felt that although Paul had asked me if I'd been all right he wasn't really thinking about me but that his thoughts were somewhere else, and that wherever that somewhere else was it was troubled and not very happy.

So what I did, I put both my arms round him, not intending to ask what was wrong, because I could see he was in one of his not-telling moods, but to try and lift him off the ground, which is a game we play and usually ends with me giggling in helpless fashion since I can't even lift him half a centimetre.

That wasn't how it ended this time. How it ended this time was Paul giving a great yell and shoving me away from him. He did it so violently that I went staggering backwards and crashed into the wall. I was really shaken, I can tell you.

I'm used to Paul being a bit moody and clamming up on me, but he's never, ever done anything like that before.

I think he was pretty shaken, too. He couldn't stop apologizing and asking me if I was all right. Any other time I might have played it up a bit, like pretending, maybe, that he'd gone and busted my arm or something, and then we'd have had what Carrie calls "a smooching session" to make things better. (I know it sounds yucky, written down like that, but wait till you're in love, you future people from another planet. It won't sound so yucky then!)

I didn't play it up because I just knew, instinctively, it wasn't the right moment. I said, "I'm OK." And then I said, "But you're not! What's the matter?" and Paul said, "Nothing," which is what he would say, even if he was dying, because that's the sort of person he is. Strong and silent. He is not a whinger. (Unlike Squirrel, who screams the place down if I even just flick him with a tea-towel.)

I said, "So why did you yell?" and he mumbled, "Doesn't matter. 'Tisn't anything," but before he could stop me, I'd grabbed at his sweater and pulled it up. All down one side he was covered in these really horrible bruises, black and blue and turning purple. I shrieked, "God, what happened?" Paul said, "Nothing! I told you!"

I could see he didn't want to talk about it, but there are times when you have to. Even if he got mad at me, I had to find out. You don't get bruises like that from just nowhere.

I said, "What do you mean, nothing? You look as if a bus ran into you."

In the end, when I kept on at him, he muttered that he had been mugged on the way home on Saturday. I was horrified. I said, "Where?" He said it had happened as he was turning into the Estate.

"There was a couple of 'em ... white guys. About sixteen. Waiting for me." I said, "You mean they knew you were coming?" Paul said no, they were just hanging around waiting for anyone who looked a likely target.

"Any road, they didn't get anything. That's one satisfaction."

"No," I said, "because you didn't have anything for them to get." Paul never has anything. Money, I mean, or valuables. "They still beat you up!" I said.

I thought it was his pride that was more hurt than anything and that was why he didn't want to talk about it. I suppose it is quite belittling for a bloke to be beaten up by other blokes.

I said, "Were they off the Estate? Could you identify them?" but Paul said he'd never seen them before. He also said that he hadn't bothered reporting it to the police. "What's the point? What could they do about it?"

I knew it wasn't any use arguing and telling him that he should; he would only have gone all moody on me, which is what he does when we have disagreements. The police are one of the things we disagree about. I've been brought up to believe that the police are there for our protection; Paul's been brought up to believe that they're out to get you. We're always having ding-dongs about it. I once tried saying, "Suppose someone broke into your place and burgled it? I bet you'd go running to them fast enough then!"

But people on the Estate don't go anywhere near the police if they can help it. They get burgled all the time and they just put up with it. They fix these bars and padlocks on their doors and if they're old folk they never go out after dark, and if they're ethnic minorities they live in terror, and if they're young everyone thinks they're thugs or junkies, and if they're single mums they've only got pregnant to get themselves a council flat (that's what my nan says) and they don't have Neighbourhood Watch like the rest of us, or friendly coppers coming round to tell you how to make your place burglar-proof. You couldn't be burglar-proof, I shouldn't think, on the Estate. If the burglars couldn't break the door open, they'd most likely just stuff burning rags through the letter box. That's what my nan says.

So I knew it wasn't any good going on at Paul. He'd only have got in a sulk and called me middle class and over-privileged. I've tried telling him that I don't see how I *can* be called that when I live in a council flat same as him, but Paul says our block is where all the snob families are put. He says it's a "showpiece" block, because it has things like entryphones and proper garages, and there are carpet squares on the walls of the lifts.

I suppose he is right; it never occurred to me before. I thought everybody had entryphones and proper garages, but perhaps they do not.

It is difficult when people come from different backgrounds. When I was little I used to think it would be tremendously romantic if someone like a royal prince, say, were to fall in love with me and ask me to become his wife, but now I don't as I begin to see that his family would probably regard me as dead common for living in a council flat, even if it does have carpet in the lift.

I, on the other hand, do not regard Paul as being dead common for living on the Estate. It doesn't bother me one little bit, except when he accuses me of being middle class or a snob (which I am *not*). So whenever it looks as if we are going to start an argument, I always back down very quickly before he can begin accusing me.

This is what I did that Monday when he came to school covered in purple bruises and said that he'd been mugged. When he said, "What's the point?" I backed down immediately. I said, "I suppose you're right. I suppose the police couldn't really do anything." It wasn't actually what I thought, but I didn't want to start an argument.

What bothered me more than him not going to the police was that he hadn't been to the doctor, either. I said, "For all you know, you could have a broken rib," but Paul said it was only bruises and he wasn't going to the doctor because he didn't believe in doctors, which I think is just plain daft, but when he is in a certain sort of mood it is impossible to reason with him. Best not to try.

He said, "I don't want you going round blabbing to folk," and I promised that I wouldn't. I thought that it was silly to feel ashamed of being beaten up when you have been set upon by two guys who are much older than you are and have taken you by surprise in any case, but Paul has always had a lot of pride. It is just the way he is. Because, I suppose, of coming from the Estate and always having to prove himself.

I swore I wouldn't say a word to a soul, and I didn't, even though it unfairly got me into hot water with Mick Andrews, who is in the sixth form and the school games captain. He came up to me at lunchtime, when I was walking round the playground with Carrie. (We always stick together during the lunch break. Paul is usually kicking a ball around with the other lads.) Carrie saw him coming and turned bright beetroot, because she has this terrific thing about him, but it was me he wanted to talk to, not her. He said, "Tracey Blair! I'd like a word with you," and he moved me off across the playground so that poor old pink-faced Carrie couldn't hear, which in fact was just as well.

He was in the most frightful rage. He said, "I'm well pleased with you!" in tones which indicated he was anything *but*. More likely well something else beginning with a p, which he would probably like to have said but thought he'd better not, being a prefect and all.

He said that Paul had just told him he wouldn't be able to attend football practice after school because he was going somewhere with me. He said, "It's just not good enough!" He told me I was being selfish and trying to keep Paul tied to my apron strings. He said I'd grow up to be a jealous woman and that I ought to stop thinking of myself and start thinking of the school.

I really resented this and I did think Paul might have told me he was going to use me as an excuse, but I kept my promise to him. I didn't tell Mick the real reason Paul couldn't attend his stupid football practice was that he'd gone and got himself mugged and was covered in bruises.

Mick stamped off, muttering about "possessive women", and old Carrie comes flying across the playground all agog and desperate to know what he'd said.

"Did he want you to play for the girls' football team? I wouldn't mind playing for the girls' football team! Did you say that I'd like to?"

I said it wasn't anything to do with the girls' football team. (And even if it had been I wouldn't have mentioned Carrie, because he'd only have laughed. Carrie is far too round and chubby to play football. I wouldn't lay her open to such humiliation.)

Of course, she insisted on knowing what he'd wanted to speak to me about. I suppose I could have said it was none of her business, but you don't treat your friends that way and in any case I'd have wanted to know if it had been her he'd spoken to instead of me. So I said, "Oh, he'd just got his Y-fronts in a twist 'cause he reckons Paul's spending too much time with me and not enough time practising," which immediately appealed to the romantic side of Carrie's nature.

She said, "Oh, it must be so wonderful being in love!"

It is, but it is not always easy. You have to make sacrifices (like letting Mick Andrews think I am a possessive woman) and you don't always even get thanked for it. When I told Paul what had happened, he just said that "Mick Andrews is a *******." (The stars are instead of a bad word.) And when I suggested that now we could walk home together, since he wasn't going to football practice, he said that he couldn't because he had to get back. What he usually does is walk to the flats with me and then get on a bus that takes him to the Estate. But that day he said he couldn't. He didn't say why he couldn't; he just said he couldn't. He didn't even say that he was sorry. For using me as an excuse, that is. *And* for not walking home with me. He did give me a kiss, but it was only a very quick one. More of a peck, really, than a proper kiss. And then he went racing off and that was the last time I saw him until –

Well, until after it had all happened. Until the police came and interviewed me in Mr Smethurst's office and made it seem like Paul was a criminal, or even worse.

chapter **three**

I HAVE discovered why it is that books have chapters. It is so that you can stop for a bit and work out what you are going to write next.

I am going to write about what happened at school on Tuesday. Paul wasn't there for morning assembly, and he still wasn't there for French, which is what we have just before break on a Tuesday.

I was worried, because it isn't like Paul to be away. In spite of coming from the Estate he doesn't ever skive off (lots of the kids do) and in spite of his mum not feeding him properly he isn't ever ill. I was worried in case one of his ribs had been broken from the mugging and he had had to go to hospital. It wouldn't have surprised me if one of them had been smashed. I'd never seen anyone bruised as badly as Paul was: it looked like he had been thrown to the floor and kicked.

We'd only been in French about ten minutes when Mrs James, who is one of the school secretaries, came into the room and whispered at Mr Barker, and Mr Barker nodded and said, "Tracey!" in annoyed tones. "Mr Smethurst would like to see you."

I'm really glad we don't have one of those loudspeaker systems they have in some schools. I would have died if this voice had suddenly come booming out, "Tracey Blair to Mr Smethurst's office!" It was bad enough as it was. Everyone slewed round in their desks to watch as I left the room. I knew they were thinking I'd done something dire. Probably they were thinking that I'd been caught in possession of drugs, which is something I shall never be. No way! I am not going to smoke, I am not going to drink, I am not going to take drugs. Nor is Ess; we have decided. It is a mug's game.

Another thing they may have been thinking was that something awful had happened to Mum or Dad, because last term a girl called Alice Roper was called to see Mr Smethurst and we heard later that her mum had been killed in a car crash. Fortunately I didn't remember this until now. If I had thought about it at the time, I would have been convinced that that was what it was. I am not a natural-born pessimist like Ess (who always fears the worst), but it is very rare and unusual to be called out of class, so whatever it was I knew it had to be something serious.

Maybe Mrs James was remembering about Alice, because when we reached Mr Smethurst's door she said, "You'll find a policewoman in there, Tracey, but there's no need to be scared. It's nothing you've done. She just wants to ask you a few questions."

Mr Smethurst was looking grim, but then he always does. He just has one of these grim sort of faces, very long and leathery, with creases. He's OK, really; I quite like him.

The policewoman was young and prettyish. (I have thought of joining the police, only I might not be tall enough and anyway Paul would hate it, so probably instead I may try to be an airline pilot. If my maths is good enough!!!)

Mr Smethurst said, "Take a seat, Tracey. This is Police Constable Deare. She'd like you to help her, if you can. It seems that your friend Paul has gone missing and has taken his little sister with him. I wonder if you can shed any light on it?"

I know in books when people are given startling pieces of information they always write that "their jaw fell open" or "they stared, wide-eyed". I don't *think* my jaw fell open, but I probably stared. I mean, it just didn't make any sense. Paul? Missing? Why would Paul want to go missing? And if he did, why take Lily with him? She's only three years old!

The policewoman told me that "He took the little girl down to the shops at four o'clock yesterday afternoon and never came back. We wondered if he'd been in touch with you at all? If he'd ever said anything about running away from home?"

I said that he hadn't, which was true. And then I said, "How do you know he's run away?"

The policewoman admitted that they didn't, for sure. But she said that someone had seen Paul and Lily walking down the road, and that they had walked straight past the supermarket where they were supposed to have been going. She said, "We're obviously very anxious to find them, so anything you can tell us would be most helpful."

She refused to believe I couldn't tell them anything. She started asking me all these questions, like when did I last go round to Paul's place and how often had I seen him on his own with Lily? She seemed surprised when I said that I had never been round to his place and that I had never seen him with Lily. She said in that case did he ever *talk* about Lily, to which I said no. Never.

She said, "You know, of course, that the little girl is mentally handicapped?"

That sort of took me by surprise and I said no, I didn't, which took *her* by surprise. She said, "I thought you and Paul were very close to each other?"

I said that we were but that I had only seen Lily once and that Paul had never told me she was handicapped. I said probably he didn't like to talk about it, and she agreed that he probably didn't. Then she asked me if I could think of anywhere he might have gone or might be heading, and I racked my brains but I couldn't. He doesn't have any aunts or uncles or grandparents.

I told the policewoman this and she said yes, she was aware, but she thought he might perhaps have a place where he liked to go, like a secret den or a hideaway.

I didn't say that secret dens and hideaways were the sort of things you had in Juniors; I thought it might sound rude. So I just said again that I didn't know. (I wasn't going to tell her about our meeting places, though I looked in them later and of course he wasn't there.)

I could tell she didn't feel I was being very helpful, but it wasn't my fault. I suppose I could have explained that the reason I never went to Paul's place was that he was ashamed of living on the Estate, only I wasn't even sure that it was. The reason, I mean. I'd just always assumed it, but that was before I'd heard about Lily. Maybe it was Lily he was ashamed of. I know that people sometimes are, when there's handicaps. My Auntie Maureen has a son that's Down's Syndrome and for ages and ages we were never allowed to go there. (Now we go quite often, because Nan had a go at her, and me and Danny are really good friends. *I* don't mind being seen with him. He's fun and makes me laugh! We have great times together.)

I thought it would be sad if Paul was ashamed of his little sister, but even if he was that didn't explain why he should have taken her down to the shops and not come back. I said, "I don't think he'd get into a car with anyone." Not unless he knew them. But why had he walked past the supermarket?

The policewoman said, "You realize we are very concerned for the little girl's safety?" She didn't say they were concerned for Paul's safety. I didn't understand that. Why be concerned for Lily and not for Paul?

Mr Smethurst said, "All right, Tracey. You can go now. But please don't hesitate to come and tell me if you suddenly think of anything. It doesn't matter how insignificant it may seem, we'd like to know about it. Yes?"

As I was going through the door I remembered about Paul being mugged and I wondered if that was the sort of thing Mr Smethurst wanted to know about. But it didn't seem to have anything to do with Paul and Lily disappearing, and besides, I'd promised Paul I wouldn't tell, so I left the room without mentioning it.

Carrie was waiting for me, anxiously hovering outside the office. We went into the playground together and I told her what had happened (but not about the mugging). Carrie is an optimistic soul. She said that she was sure there must be some simple explanation. She said, "Nothing could happen to Paul!" And then, as an afterthought, she added, "Did you know he had a sister?"

I said that I did, but that I hadn't realized she was handicapped. But suddenly I was beginning to remember the one and only time that I'd seen her. It was back in Year 7, before Paul and I were properly together. I'd gone into town with Mum and we were walking through the Pallisades, which is a shopping centre just next to New Street Station, when we saw Paul and his mum and stepdad and this little kid in a pushchair. I didn't really look at the little kid, or at Paul's mum or stepdad. (Too busy looking at Paul!) I could just vaguely remember his stepdad because I remember thinking he looked a bit like Ess's favourite movie star, Tom Hanks. I couldn't remember his mum or Lily at all. I mean, I know *now* what his mum looks like, but I couldn't remember her from that particular day.

We didn't stop and talk, we just said hallo and walked on. But as soon as we were out of earshot Mum said, "There's something not right about that child." She said it almost accusingly, as if it was a thing they'd been trying to keep from us. "Definitely not right."

I'd forgotten all about it. I suppose I wouldn't have, if Paul had ever talked about his little sister, but he never did. Carrie, who wasn't at Juniors with us, didn't even know he had one. Yet when his mum was expecting, he was really excited about it. We had to write essays one time and Paul wrote one about how his mum was going to have a baby and Miss Martin read it out in class and we all discussed whether we'd rather have brothers or sisters or be only children. I said, "Be an only child," thinking of Ess and being just about sick to death of having Squirrel for a brother. Paul, on the other hand, said *he* thought having a brother or sister would be fun. (Some of us groaned when he said that.)

And then Lily had been born and from that day on he had never talked about her.

The more I think about it, the more I think how sad it is. I mean sad for Paul, but sad for Lily, too. I don't *think* I would have been ashamed of Squirrel if he'd been born handicapped. I think I would have loved him all the more. (Because I do love him, really, in spite of his irritating ways.)

That evening I went upstairs to Ess's flat to have what my nan calls "a chinwag". I had to confide in *someone*. Someone other than Carrie, that is. Carrie is a sweet and dear and beautiful person, but she is so eager to please that quite often she will just say the first thing that occurs to her to make you happy. Like, for instance, assuring me that nothing could happen to Paul. If I'd asked her why not, she wouldn't have had the faintest idea. It was just something she said to stop me worrying. But I *was* worried, all the same, and I had to talk to someone.

Normally I'd have talked to Mum, because Mum is a really understanding sort of person and almost always sympathetic. I once came home from Juniors in the most terrible panic because I'd gone nicking in Woolie's with a girl called Primrose Harbottle (that truly was her name, I kid you not) and afterwards remorse and terror had overcome me and I was sure the police were going to turn up on the doorstep and arrest me.

Even then, Mum wasn't mad. She just said that I'd obviously given myself a fright but that at least it had taught me a lesson and she hoped she could trust me never to do such a thing again, which I never have. (Primrose Harbottle did and got caught and serves her right. I told her she was asking for trouble.)

Oh, and Mum made me give the stuff I'd nicked to Oxfam. She said I couldn't repent *and* keep my ill-gotten gains.

But I didn't feel like telling Mum about Paul because I have always been convinced in my heart that she disapproves of him and I felt that this would make her disapprove even more, so I went upstairs and unburdened myself to Ess instead.

Ess is a pretty good listener, and although she couldn't come up with an explanation, at least she didn't offer words of false comfort. She said, "Paul isn't stupid, so I'm sure he wouldn't have gone off with anyone." She suggested that maybe he had had a row at home. "That's usually why people run away. I've been reading about it."

I remembered that Paul *did* have rows with his stepdad. "But why take Lily?" Ess said, "Maybe he didn't mean to take her, he just suddenly decided, on the spur of the moment." I said, "You mean, on the way to the shops? He suddenly thought he'd run away?" Ess said, "It happens like that."

It was the only explanation we could come up with; the only one that wasn't horrible and scary.

Ess said I wasn't to think of things that were horrible and scary, such as someone offering a lift and Paul accepting it, or someone jumping out of a car and abducting them both.

"There's no point in torturing yourself. He'll probably be back at school tomorrow and then you can come and tell me what really happened."

He wasn't back at school and I tortured myself all day long. It was like a horror movie was going on inside my head, *Silence of the Lambs* and *House of Horror* and Stephen King all muddled up together, and then that night it was on the news. "West Midlands police are growing increasingly concerned for the safety of," etc. etc., just like I'd heard a million times before, only in the past it had always been about other kids that I didn't know. And they still didn't seem to care what had happened to Paul; only to Lily.

"... increasingly concerned for the safety of Lily Redwood, aged three and a quarter, who disappeared with her half-brother, Paul, from their Aston home on Monday evening."

And then they went on to tell the story of how Lily and Paul had set off for the supermarket at four o'clock and not come back, and how people had seen them walking straight past the supermarket and carrying on down the road. One woman reported that Paul had been holding Lily's hand and had seemed to be "dragging her". Another woman said that she thought Lily had been crying.

"I couldn't swear to it, but her little face was all puckered."

It made shivers go tingling down my spine when she said that. And the bit about Paul holding Lily's hand and "dragging her". It made it sound as if she hadn't wanted to go with him; as if Paul had forced her. It sounded ... sinister.

Mum was there with me when the news came on. (Dad was still out working. He was on late shift.) She said, "Tracey! Did you know about this?" She couldn't understand why I hadn't told her. I didn't say it was because I didn't think she approved of Paul. I just muttered something about "hoping he'd have turned up".

"They're obviously worried about the little girl," said Mum. They'd reported her as "handicapped" and Mum couldn't help reminding me that it was what she had said all those months ago.

"I knew there was something not right. You

could tell." She wasn't gloating; just kind of proud that she'd been sharp enough to spot it.

I said, "But why are they only worried about her and not about Paul?"

"Likely they think he's capable of looking after himself. But a poor little mite like that – " Mum shook her head. "He'd no right to go carting her off with him."

"Maybe he couldn't bear to leave her behind," I said.

"Why?" said Mum. "Was he fond of her? I've never heard him talk of her, all the times he's been round here. And if he was, it's a strange way to show it, taking her away from her mum and dad."

"Maybe he didn't mean to." I was getting desperate by now. I told Mum the theory that Ess and I had come up with, that Paul had had a row with his mum or his stepdad, or both, and suddenly decided, on the way to the shops, that he had had enough and was going to do a bunk. "And so he had to take Lily with him."

It sounded lame even as I said it. Mum just snorted.

"Ought to be horsewhipped. I don't care if he did have a row. There's nothing can justify taking a little kiddy like that from its parents. My God, that poor woman! What she must be going through! You just imagine if someone were to make off with our Squirrel."

I pointed out that it wasn't "someone", it was Paul, and he was Lily's brother, but it cut no ice with Mum. She just said, "All the more shame on him," especially as Lily was handicapped.

I said I didn't see that her being handicapped made it any worse, necessarily, but Mum snapped that of course it did! She said that any mother would feel extra specially protective towards a handicapped child and that Paul's mum must be going through agony. She said, "I just hope when they finally catch up with him he's still got her safe. And they'd better not let him off lightly! Today it's his sister, tomorrow who knows? Deserves to be locked up and the key thrown away, if you ask me."

I'd never heard Mum be so vituperative before. She really made it sound as if she hated Paul. As if he was some kind of lout or pervert. I know why it was: she'd gone and lashed herself into a state imagining how it would be if someone were to run off with Squirrel. Squirrel is *definitely* her favourite. It's because he's so weak and weedy, I guess. You couldn't exactly call him handicapped, but she's certainly protective towards him.

I don't mind, as a rule; not really. But it did make me mad when she went on about Paul deserving to be locked up. I couldn't talk to her any more after that. I went to bed.

Next morning it was on breakfast telly, so I knew I wasn't going to get to school and find that Paul had come back. Of course, everyone had heard the news, or if they hadn't they'd been told about it. In the playground they were all looking at me and whispering. I knew they were pointing me out as "the girl that goes round with Paul Redwood". I tried to pretend that I didn't care.

Needless to say, all the kids in our class were dead curious and dying to ask questions, but most of them weren't bold enough. It was only Clive Meldrum who had the brass face to come up and say, "So what's it all about, then? Where is he?" He wouldn't believe me when I said I didn't know. Nobody believed me. They all thought I was keeping quiet because Paul had sworn me to silence.

Miss Tench, our year group tutor, obviously thought the same, because at break I was called in to see her, and the policewoman was there again, so I knew it was going to be an interrogation session.

Miss Tench is nice. She's quite young and dresses *really* fashionably and doesn't bully or bark like some of them. She said she was aware that I'd been interviewed before and had said I didn't know anything, but now she wanted me to think "very, very carefully" because a child's life could be at stake.

"The police are seriously concerned, Tracey. They think the little girl could be in danger."

I said, "I'm sure if she's with Paul he'll take care of her."

The policewoman pounced on that. She said, "Have you any idea how Paul feels about his sister?"

I said no, but he was really good with Squirrel. I said, "Squirrel is my brother and is a complete pain. I'm always getting mad at him, but Paul never does."

Miss Tench, quite gently, pointed out that Squirrel wasn't handicapped and that in any case it was sometimes easier to be good with other people's brothers and sisters than with your own.

I said, "Yes, but even my best friend, Esther,

gets mad at Squirrel. He once tore some pages out of a book she'd lent me and it was one of her favourites. Mum just said I shouldn't have left it where he could get at it. She never tells him off. He's spoilt rotten."

"And you resent it." Miss Tench nodded. "That's only natural. We all feel hard done by at times. Paul probably did, when his mum and dad made a fuss of Lily. It must have been difficult for him, don't you think? For nearly ten years he has his mum all to himself, then suddenly she gets married again and has a baby, and everyone's making a fuss of the new arrival and not taking very much notice of Paul ... It wouldn't be surprising if Paul felt a bit left out, would it? Do you think?"

I frowned. What was she trying to say?

"It often causes problems, when there's a handicapped child in the family." That was the policewoman, shoving her oar in. "The siblings feel jealous because the one that's handicapped gets all the attention."

I didn't know for sure what siblings were (just brothers and sisters, I *think*) but I got her drift: she was trying to say that Paul had been jealous of Lily.

And that was why he had kidnapped her?

The thought came from nowhere. I did my best to banish it.

"Did he *never* mention his little sister to you?" said Miss Tench.

I said no, he didn't, which was what I'd said before, and Miss Tench said, "Didn't that strike you as rather odd?"

I said no, not really. I don't think most boys of thirteen would talk about their sisters. Not if the sisters were only three and a bit.

I was going to say this to Miss Tench, but she got in first. She said, "Tracey, I know that you and Paul are very close to each other, but you must see that there is grave cause for concern. It would be totally wrong to keep silent out of some kind of mistaken loyalty. A child's life is in danger here."

I said again, "I'm sure Paul will look after her." I expect I sounded stubborn, but I didn't care. They were asking me the same questions over and over and I didn't like the way they kept hinting things about Paul.

There was a silence after I'd spoken. Miss Tench and the policewoman exchanged glances (they thought they were doing it over my head, but I saw them). Then the policewoman cleared her throat and said, "We do have reason to believe – that is, according to the boy's step-father – "

I really hated her for referring to Paul as "the boy". She must have felt it, because she went back and corrected herself.

She told me that "Paul's stepfather" had made a statement saying that on several occasions he'd caught Paul ill-treating Lily. "Slapping her, pinching her, pushing her around." He'd said that a few weeks ago they'd discovered red marks all over her after she'd been left alone with him. "As if someone had used her for stubbing out cigar-ettes."

I snapped, "Paul doesn't smoke!" which I suppose was a bit of a stupid sort of thing to say, really, but it was all I could think of. Not that she took any notice. She just went on telling me all these awful things that Paul was supposed to have done, like one time he had picked Lily up and shaken her and another time he had yelled at her that he wished she was dead.

And then on Saturday night, at about quarter-past ten, the next-door neighbour had heard the sound of a child screaming. She hadn't rung the police because people on the Estate never did, and after a bit it had stopped. But when Paul's mum and stepdad came back a while later, they found Lily cowering in her bed, terrified and covered all over in dreadful wheels.

(Weals? Maybe that is how you spell it.)

"Apparently the stepfather lost his temper and gave Paul what he calls 'a right lamming'. Then Monday evening both Paul and the little girl disappeared. So you can see," said the policewoman, "why it is that we're so concerned."

Miss Tench said, "Put your head between your knees, Tracey, if you feel faint."

I've never fainted; never in my life. But I almost did then.

It was the shock of hearing all those things about Paul. However much I kept saying to myself that I didn't believe it, I couldn't help remembering how he'd come in to school on Monday covered in bruises.

Miss Tench said, "Is there anything you want to tell us, Tracey?"

And the policewoman said, "You mustn't feel you're being disloyal. Think of it this way: you might be saving a life."

I didn't tell them about the bruises; there wasn't any point. Paul's stepdad had already said how he'd lammed him.

I just said that I was very sorry, but I still couldn't think of a single thing that would be helpful.

I knew they didn't believe me, any more than anyone else had. Miss Tench said that if I *did* think of anything I was to come straight back to her, and the policewoman said that if Paul got in touch with me I was to ring them. I said that I would and went away feeling dazed.

I couldn't concentrate on classes. My mind was spinning like a Catherine wheel. There was something that was bothering me, but I couldn't think what it was.

A sort of inkling came to me in the middle of geography (which is a subject I happen to loathe as I am particularly bad at it). I thought, "Paul was with me on Saturday night!"

If he was with me, and his mum and stepdad were out, did that mean that Lily had been left on her own?

I knew what Nan would say. She would say that that was "typical of them on the Estate". Maybe it was. Maybe they really did behave the way everyone said they behaved, like going up to the pub to get drunk and leaving their children indoors without anyone to watch over them.

I thought, maybe that was why Paul had been so eager to go home, so that he could beat up Lily before his mum and stepdad got back.

But I still didn't believe it.

And then suddenly, in maths, it came to me: the neighbour had heard Lily screaming at "about quarter-past ten". But Paul hadn't left me until half-past! The earliest he could have arrived home was quarter to eleven.

That meant he couldn't possibly have done what they accused him of doing. If Lily had screamed, it must either have been because she had woken up and found herself on her own and been frightened, or because someone else had been there, doing things to her.

But whoever it was, it couldn't have been Paul.

chapter **four**

I DIDN'T know what to do. I didn't need anyone to tell me what I *ought* to do. What I ought to do was go straight to Miss Tench. But I was scared that they would put me on the news, like the woman who thought she'd seen Lily crying, and then Mum would discover that I'd been telling lies.

But I couldn't let them go round accusing Paul when I knew that he was innocent. I had to do something!

It would have helped if Ess had been there; I can talk to Ess as I can't to Carrie. It is really annoying that we go to different schools, but Ess is so incredibly brainy. She went and won this scholarship, which meant that we were separated.

So I had to struggle by myself, having a battle with my conscience. I was already feeling really guilty, because of having deceived Mum; I'd feel even more guilty if I let the police go on believing that Paul had beaten Lily up.

What I was desperately trying to work out was whether there was some way I could clear Paul's name without having to give myself away to Mum.

At last – in the middle of RE this time, but that was all right, Mr Carter probably thought my vague and abstracted expression was due to the fact that I was thinking about God – at last it came to me how I might be able to do it. What I thought was, if I went round to the Estate and spoke to Paul's mum, and told her how I had an alibi for Paul, then maybe she would go to the police and tell them without me having to become involved. Or at least without me having to be on the news. Of course, she would have to admit that she had left Lily on her own.

It wouldn't clear Paul of all the other things they had accused him of, I realized that. But at least they couldn't go on saying that he was guilty of this one particular thing.

I still didn't believe he was guilty of the other things, either.

At the end of the school day I went down the

road to a phone box and called Mum. I told her I'd be a bit late as there was something I had to stay on for. It wasn't a lie; there *was* something I had to stay on for. Mum probably thought it was a school thing, but I didn't actually say that it was.

After I'd rung Mum, I took a bus to the Estate. It's only about a mile away and Paul usually walks in the mornings, to save his bus fare, but I wasn't sure of the route and besides, I was in a hurry. I wanted to get to the Estate and speak to Paul's mum before his stepdad got in. (I'm not absolutely certain what Paul's stepdad does but I think he works on the buildings, because once when Ess and I were in town we stopped at a building site to peer through one of those observation windows they put in for the public, so they can see what's going on, and we spotted someone who looked just like Tom Hanks pushing a wheelbarrow up a gangplank. Of course, there may be lots of people who look like Tom Hanks, for all I know.)

It was the first time I had ever set foot on the Estate and, to tell you the truth, I was quite frightened. I kept thinking that yobs were going to appear out of nowhere and start mugging me, but in fact all that happened was that a vicious-looking dog wearing a muzzle came up and sniffed at me until a child about two centimetres high yelled "Buster-you-come-'ere!" and it went ambling off ever so meekly, wagging its tail. I am almost sure it was a pit bull terrier, which just goes to show that appearances can be deceptive. They are not all evil, horrible creatures and Ess is right when she says you shouldn't tar everyone with the same brush, though she probably wouldn't say that about dogs since she happens to be terrified of them, even Yorkshire terriers.

I am not in the least bit terrified of dogs (Paul has taught me not to be; he always goes out of his way to talk to them). What I was more terrified of was getting into the lift all by myself. The lifts on the Estate don't have carpet on the walls. They are like big tin boxes, all rattling and jerky. Everywhere you look, people have sprayed graffiti – some of them just rude, but some of them quite nasty – and also they smell. I didn't like to think what it was they smelt of, so I just pressed the button to the fifth floor and prayed that the thing wouldn't get stuck or that the doors wouldn't suddenly open and a gang of muggers walk in.

When I got out on the fifth floor it was like

being in a prison. How I would imagine it would be, being in a prison. There were these long, dark corridors stretching as far as the eye could see, with dozens and dozens of doors, all painted the same horrible cheesy yellow, which perhaps was meant to look bright but in fact just looked bilious, as if someone had spewed sick everywhere. (I think someone actually may have done so. I saw some very dubious splatters up one of the walls.)

I had always known that the Estate was rough and tough, because everyone is always complaining about it, but I had never realized before that it was so dismal and squalid. I felt almost that I was cheating on Paul by being there, as if I were spying on him behind his back, and I hoped that he would never need to be told. I thought that when he came back, *if* he came back – only I wouldn't let my mind dwell on the possibility that he might not – I would never let on that I had seen where he lived.

Number 524 was right at the end of one of the long, dark corridors. (They were like concrete tunnels, with narrow slits instead of windows and dim orangy light panels let into the ceiling). I rang at the bell but it didn't seem to work, so I knocked with my fist. After a bit the door opened just a crack and a face peered out.

Paul's mum. I knew it had to be Paul's mum because she looked like Paul. She would have been quite pretty if she hadn't been so pale and what Nan would call "peaky". She would have looked better with a bit of make-up.

She said "Yes?" in tones that indicated any minute she was going to slam the door in my face, not because she was hostile so much as she was nervous. I expect on the Estate people don't like strange faces.

Very quickly, before she could shut me out, I said, "I'm Tracey, Paul's friend from school."

She said, "What do you want? Paul's not here."

I said, "No, I know, I've seen it on the news and the police have asked me questions."

Very sharply she said, "What questions?"

I told her some of the ones they'd asked, and then I told her how they'd said that a neighbour had heard screaming at about quarter-past ten. I said, "But Paul was round with me and he didn't leave until gone half-past!"

At this her eyes went all shifty, flickering to and fro, and she said, "They must have got it wrong, then. Must have been later."

So then I asked her what time she'd got in and she said, "What's it to you?" I said, "I'm trying to prove that Paul is innocent!"

There was a pause and then she said, "I can't help you," and tried to close the door, but I was too quick for her and stuck my foot in it. I said, "Suppose the neighbour got it right? Suppose it *was* only quarter-past ten? That means it couldn't possibly have been Paul! It's not fair letting the police think he's guilty. He's your son! You ought to tell them!"

At this her eyes went shifty again and she mumbled, "You tell them. I can't."

"But I'm only a kid," I said. "They won't believe me, they'll think I'm just saying it to protect him. Please! You're the one that ought to do it."

"I can't," she said. Her eyes were shooting glances over my shoulder, trying to see up the corridor, as if she was expecting hordes of killer bees or flesh-eating aliens to suddenly materialize. "You don't understand! I can't!"

I said, "But Paul is your *son*."

"I can't help it," she said. "There's nothing I can do!"

That's when she sent the door slamming into

my face. I heard the sound of bolts and padlocks, and I knew she wasn't going to open up again. I was really shocked at a grown person being so useless. Her own son and she wouldn't shift to defend him!

Of course, I was pretty useless, too; but I'm only thirteen, for heaven's sake!

I had a sort of feeling, even then, that being only thirteen wasn't all that much of an excuse. I think it was that, plus the way I feel about Paul, that gave me the courage to go and ring at the bell of number 523, the flat next door.

The bell worked, this time. A young black woman opened the door and looked at me suspiciously. I don't blame her for being suspicious; I would be, if I lived on the Estate. Specially if I was black. Paul says the police are always picking on black people. But at least she couldn't mistake me for a police person.

I said, "I'm very sorry to disturb you but my name is Tracey Blair and I go to the same school as Paul Redwood. The police have been asking me questions and I was just wondering if you could possibly remember what time it was when you heard the screams."

She said, "I already told the police all I know. Ten-fifteen is what I told them."

"Can you be absolutely positive?" I said. It was important I knew. She had to be positive.

A look of distinct annoyance came over her face. I could tell she was just about sick of being asked questions. (Me too! I sympathized with her. I knew how she felt.)

She said, "*Yes*. How many more times? Once and for all . . . I'm absolutely positive. If you want to know, I looked at the clock and I thought, they're off again. I was gonna bang on the wall, but then it stopped. What do you want to know for, anyway?"

I told her that Paul's mum had said she must have made a mistake, it must have been later than quarter-past ten, and she tossed her head and said, "Her! She wouldn't know what day of the week it was."

So I knew then what I ought to do, but I still couldn't make up my mind to do it. I went home and sat in a trance in front of the telly, eating my tea and arguing with myself that telling the police Paul had been with me wasn't going to help them find him. Also, unless I could prove it to them, they would be bound to say I was making it up, and the only way I could prove it was by involving Ess, which would get *her* into trouble because she'd told lies for me. She'd told Mum I was in the loo when I was downstairs in the flat with Paul.

There was always her-next-door, old Nosy Parker Gullick. She could confirm my story. She'd been there as usual, spying on us as Paul went out. But she'd go and blab to Mum, sure as eggs, if she thought it was going to get me into trouble.

Chances were, the police would want all of us, me and Mum, and Ess and her-next-door, to tesstify (testify?) about times. Mum could say when she rang from Auntie Ellen's, and Ess could say what time she came down to the flat to give us Mum's message, and old Nosy P. could say what time she saw Paul and me heading for the lift. Then they would know for sure that Paul couldn't have been home by quarter-past ten.

I was still whizzing it all about in my mind, trying to pluck up the courage to do what I knew was right, when there was a knock at the door and I nearly fell out of my chair. I was convinced it was the police, coming to tell me that they had found Paul and Lily hacked to pieces in a ditch, but it wasn't the police, it was Ess.

It was very annoying, because for ages Mum hovered in the doorway trying to engage Ess in conversation, saying banal things such as "How are you getting on at school?" and "Are you still planning to be a brain surgeon?" (one of Mum's standing jokes, what with Ess being so monumentally clever). The reason it was annoying was that I could see that in fact Ess was absolutely frantic to tell me something that couldn't be told in front of Mum. So after a few minutes I said, "This is rubbish!" turning the telly off. "Let's go and listen to music."

"Don't you play it too loud!" said Mum. "I don't want Mrs Gullick complaining."

Ess just managed to contain herself until I had banged a record on the record-player and then she came bursting out with it: she had just had a telephone call and it was Paul! He had really wanted to speak to me but hadn't dared ring my number in case the police were bugging the line.

"I said I'd come and fetch you but he said no, it wasn't safe. He said could you go to him? And could you take him some money, as much as you can get together? Also, could you take him some food."

Of course, I wanted to know where he was, but Ess said he hadn't given her an address, he'd just said, "Tell her – " Ess closed her eyes and scrunched up her face as she tried to remember it right – "tell her S-for-Sugar Alpha-Foxtrot-Tango-Zero N-for-Nuts. He said you'd know what it means. *Do* you know what it means?"

Slowly I said, "I think so."

"It's all right!" cried Ess. "You don't have to tell me!" But I could see she was dying to know. Well, I would have been, in her position. After all, she was the one who'd acted as go-between, so you could say she had every right. I said, "It's the name of a road near Cannon Hill."

We'd gone for a walk there, just a few weeks earlier. We'd been strolling around, first in the park and then round the streets, looking for houses we'd like to live in. And at the same time we'd been talking about a new police series on the telly. I remember I asked Paul whether all the police used the same call signs, like when they say "Alpha-Tango-Foxtrot", or if every police force made up their own ones.

Paul had seemed to think they all used the same, and just for fun we'd started translating the number plates of all the cars that were parked, and the names of the roads that we were walking down. We didn't know what the codes were for all letters, so some we had to make up.

S-for-Sugar Alpha-Foxtrot-Tango-Zero N-for-Nuts spelt Safton. Safton Road. It must have been down there we'd come across a big old derelict house waiting to be pulled down and have a block of flats built on it. We'd gone exploring in the garden and discovered an ancient underground shelter which Paul said must have been used for air raids in the war. I'd immediately started to fantasize about living there.

I'm always doing that. Like just near us there's this sort of hut thing which says P. DAVIES TAXI SERVICE on the window. Mr P. Davies sits in there all day (except when he's actually out in his taxi), waiting for people to call in and make bookings. I'm always working out how much furniture you could get in there, whether it would be big enough to live in. (It wouldn't, but I like to imagine it.) Paul says I have a nest complex. He says I've only got to see a hole in the ground to start working out how you could live in it.

It was easy working out how you could live in

the underground shelter, at any rate in summer. I had it fully furnished by the time we left. But I would never have remembered the name of the road if Paul hadn't spelt it out ... S-for-Sugar Alpha-Foxtrot-Tango-Zero N-for-Nuts. Safton.

"Are you going to go there?" said Ess.

I said, "Yes, but I can't remember exactly where it is. Just somewhere near Cannon Hill is all I can remember."

"I'll get our A–Z!"

Ess went galloping to the door.

"What am I going to tell Mum?" I said.

Ess paused. "If I came with you, you could say we were going to look at some kittens ... a girl at school's cat's just had some. She said anyone could go round if they wanted. She lives in Northfield."

"But that's miles from Cannon Hill!"

"Not as far as all that, but we wouldn't actually be *going* there, would we?"

I said, "Oh! No. Of course not."

"Don't worry." Ess said it kindly. "I expect it's all come as a bit of a shock. Your brain isn't functioning properly. I'll go and get the A–Z."

It only occurred to me as I was gabbling to Mum about the kittens and the girl who lived in

Northfield that here I was lying again – and Ess, as well! Ess who is so *good*. It's terrible how, once you start, the lies just come pouring out.

Mum said, "All right, go and look at your kittens, but make sure you come straight back. No hanging around. You know your dad doesn't like you being out late."

Ess's mum and dad don't like her being out late, either; not when she has to go to school next day. I said, "We'll come straight back, I promise!"

"And don't go bringing any kittens with you," said Mum. "You'll set your brother's asthma off."

Squirrel has an allergy to cats – wouldn't you know it? I grumbled about it to Ess as we raced up the road to the bus stop, and she had to remind me again, "We're not *really* going to look at kittens."

"No, but if we were," I said.

Ess said that we weren't and that she had something to give me. "For Paul ... look!"

She opened her purse and took out two £10 notes. I gaped.

"Where'd you get that from?"

"I borrowed it from Mum's housekeeping

purse. She won't miss it. She doesn't go shopping till Monday and I'll have put it back by then."

"How?" I said.

"Easy! I'll take my building society book in with me tomorrow and get the money out of there."

I thought that was ever so generous of Ess. I said, "I'm sure Paul will let you have it back as soon as he can," though I couldn't for the life of me think how he was going to do it. Ess blushed and said it didn't matter. She said, "I've got £500 in there. It's what my nan left me in her will."

Unfortunately I don't have a building society account; in fact I don't have any money at all except what's in my safe, which is a special locked box that Mum and Dad bought me last Christmas. I'm always forgetting how to open it, so I've had to write the combination on a bit of paper and put it in my handkerchief drawer. But in any case I'm not very good at saving money, so all I'd been able to scrape together was £6.20.

"Well, but now he's got £26," said Ess. "That's better than a poke in the eye with a burnt stick."

She really does use the most peculiar expressions. I don't know where she gets them from.

As well as the money, we'd both brought some food. I'd brought an apple and a banana and some biscuits, Ess had a couple of oranges, a pint of milk and a packet of Maltesers. It wasn't much, but it's not easy to filch food. Ess's mum, like mine, knows exactly what's in the cupboard.

"But now he's got some money," said Ess, "he'll maybe be able to buy something."

We finally got to Cannon Hill Park and found Safton Road on the A–Z. Ess said that she would wait in the park while I went to meet Paul. She is such a truly *thoughtful* person. Dear old Carrie, in her blundering though well-meaning way, would simply have trundled along with me, but Ess said, "I don't think he'd want me to know where he's hiding. It's all right, I've brought my French homework. I'll be quite happy."

I said (sounding like Mum), "Don't talk to anyone, will you?" "Only to weird men in mackintoshes," said Ess. She can be quite funny at times.

I left her in the park, poring over French verbs, and set off down Safton Road. I couldn't remember how far along the derelict house was, it seemed much further than I had thought, but maybe that was because I was very tense and anxious. I kept looking over my shoulder expecting to see Police Constable Deare suddenly pop out of a hedge, or a police car come screeching to a halt.

When I finally reached the house I almost walked straight past it. I had this vague idea of being terribly clever and pretending I was going somewhere else, and then haring round the corner and doubling back up a side road. The only thing was, I didn't know whether there was a corner and whether I could double back, so at the last minute I changed my mind and squeezed through the gate, which was only a quarter open, having for some reason become stuck, and I slunk down the side passage into the back garden.

The garden was just as I remembered it: full of junk and overgrown. The air-raid shelter was down at the bottom, partly hidden amongst a mass of brambles.

Sitting in the entrance, waiting for me, were Paul and Lily.

chapter **five**

AS SOON as I saw Lily, I knew what Mum had meant when she said, "There's something not right with that child."

She should have been pretty. She had this gorgeous, bright gold hair, very long and thick and curly; the sort of hair that people would die for. But there was something strange about her eyes. They were small and pink and piggyish, bunched up together in a big moon-shaped face. She wasn't Down's Syndrome. I can recognize Down's Syndrome because of Danny. I didn't know what was wrong with her, but I could see that she was handicapped.

There was something else I could see, as well: she had a huge purple bruise on one arm, and masses more on her legs. The ones on her legs were quite old, because they were turning yellow;

the one on her arm was recent. But whoever had done it to her, I knew it wasn't Paul.

As soon as she saw me, Lily screamed and buried her head in Paul's shoulder; terrified, I guess, in case I was coming to take her away.

Paul was really good. He cuddled her and soothed her and stroked her hair, her beautiful golden hair, and said, "It's OK, our Lil! It's only Tracey."

Lily lifted her head and looked up at me. Her pathetic little piggy eyes were full of doubt. She said something that sounded like, "Tady?"

Paul said, "Yeah! Tracey. I told you she'd be coming, didn't I? We'll be all right, now! Don't you worry."

Then to me he said, "Did you manage to bring anything?"

I'm not sure how to describe the way he said it. He didn't say it greedily, exactly, but – eagerly. Or maybe pleadingly. Or maybe a bit of both. Eagerly because he knew I wouldn't let him down, but scared in case just for once I had.

I showed him the food I'd brought. Lily's eyes lit up and she held out her hands for the Maltesers. I opened the packet and gave them to her and she began cramming them one after another into her mouth.

"She's not starving." Paul said it defensively, as if I might be going to accuse him of not taking proper care of her. "She's just a bit peckish. We ran out of grub."

I said, "This is all we could get. Some of it came from Ess."

I watched while Paul tore open the biscuits and the carton of milk. There were a million questions I wanted to ask but I felt maybe I ought to wait till he was ready to tell me. He fed Lily with the milk before he had any himself. She found it difficult, drinking from the carton, and dribbled it all down herself, but Paul didn't get impatient. He just pulled out his handkerchief and mopped her up as if it were something he was quite used to doing.

After a bit, very hesitantly, he said, "Did you get any money?"

I nodded.

"How much?"

I said, "£26, and £20 of that came from Ess."

Paul blushed. I'd never seen him do that before, but I think he was dead ashamed of having to beg, and especially from Ess. He said,

"I'll see she gets it back. Tell her! I'll give it back."

I said that I would tell her. I didn't ask him *how* he was going to give it her back. I just knew that he had to believe that he was. It was his pride, and I could understand that.

What I couldn't understand was why he had run away or what he was going to do. I said, "The police asked me questions."

Paul looked up, sharply. "About me?"

"You and Lily. They wanted to know if you ever talked about her and if I knew where you were."

"What'd you say?"

"I said I didn't know."

"What'd you say about me talking about her?"

"I said you didn't."

"So what'd they say to that?"

"They said – " I suddenly came rushing out with it – "They said they thought you might have run off with her because you were jealous."

"*Jealous?*" I remember Paul stopping in the act of putting the milk carton to his lips. I remember him spluttering and milk dripping off his chin. I remember he said, "Me?" and wiped his chin on the sleeve of his sweater. "Jealous of Lil?"

I mumbled, "Because of being an only child for so long."

Paul said, "Did you believe 'em?"

"No, of course I didn't!" I was upset that he should think so, even just for a moment. "It's the police! They're going on television, getting people to say how they saw you going off with Lily and how she was crying. They're trying to say she's in danger."

Paul said, "What of?"

There was a silence. I couldn't bring myself to say it.

"I'll tell you something," said Paul. "She *was* in danger, but she isn't now. Not now she's with me. You're all right now, aren't you, our kid? Not frightened any more? 'Cause you've got me to look after you."

He hugged Lily closer, but by this time old Lil was well stuck into her Maltesers and couldn't have cared less.

"What else are they saying?"

I told him they were trying to make out that he'd beaten Lily up on Saturday night. I said that one of the neighbours had heard Lily screaming at quarter-past ten and that Paul's stepdad was claiming he'd come back and caught him at it and lashed out at him.

Paul said angrily, "That's not true!"

I assured him that I knew that. I said, "It couldn't be because you were still round at our place at half-past."

He said. "It couldn't be anyway! I've never laid a finger on our Lil.'"

I said, "I told them you wouldn't." And then I confessed that I hadn't yet been brave enough to tell anyone that he had been with me but that I would, I'd go and do it straight away if Paul would only come back with me, and bring Lily with him, because I just couldn't see how they were going to survive on only £26, and come to that, I still didn't see why they had run away in the first place.

It was then that Paul told me: he'd run away because he was scared Lily would end up dead.

He said, "If you wanna know who's bin battering her, it's that bast'd calls himself me stepdad. He's always doing it! He goes out and he gets plastered, then he comes back and he bashes her! And he bashes me and me mam as well, if we try to stop him. I hate the bast'd!"

When he told me that, everything suddenly fell into place. I realized why it was he'd gone racing off in a panic at half-past ten, trying to get home before his stepdad arrived back from the pub. I realized why his mum had acted like she was terrified, and why Paul had come to school on Monday covered in welts and bruises. His stepdad *had* lashed out at him – but not because he'd caught Paul knocking Lily about, but because Paul had caught him.

Paul told me it had been going on for months. And it was when he said that that I started to remember things ... the time he had come to school with half his face cut open and had had to be carted off to hospital to have it stitched up again. (Bumped into a brick wall, he'd *said*.) The time he'd turned up with a black eye and everyone had automatically assumed he'd been in a fight. The time he chipped a front tooth "falling up the kerb". It all came back to me and I wondered how I could have been so stupidly blind. Nobody but nobody is that accident prone.

Paul said that just lately it had got so bad he was really frightened that something terrible would happen – not to himself, but to Lily.

"I was scared he'd end up killing her. Look!"

He rolled up her jumper and I saw that all her ribs were black and blue, just like Paul's had been. But it looked even worse on a kid Lily's age.

I couldn't get to grips with it. I just couldn't understand how anyone could want to hurt a poor little kid like Lily. What harm had she ever done?

Paul said she'd never done any harm at all – "just existed". He said his stepdad couldn't stand having her about the place. She got on his nerves because she was clumsy and she cried a lot and sometimes chucked her food about the place and messed the bed.

Paul said, "She can't help it! It's not her fault, she's just a bit slow. If she wasn't so terrified all the time, she wouldn't do half these things. It's because she's scared of being hammered."

I suppose I'm quite naïve really, but I told Paul that what he ought to do was come back with me and tell the police. I guess I had these visions that they would immediately go and arrest his stepdad so that Paul and Lily could return home.

Paul just laughed, except that it wasn't an amused kind of laugh. More like sardonic, or maybe sarcastic. Something like that.

He said, "You must be joking! They'd never take my word against his, and me mam's too terrified to talk."

I didn't tell him that I thought his mum was totally and utterly useless. I said that if I went to the police and admitted he'd been round my place at the time he was supposed to have been bashing Lily, then they'd *have* to believe it. Paul said, "That's what you think!" He said they'd simply accuse me of making it up.

I pointed out that Ess had been there. "She could tell them! And that horrible old hag Mrs Gullick. She was spying on us as you left. They couldn't say *she* was making it up!"

Paul still wouldn't budge. He muttered that he didn't trust the police. He said, "Me mam went to them one time because he beat up on her and they didn't do a thing."

So then I had another idea. I said, "What about the social services?"

Paul said the social services were rubbish. He said they were worse than useless. "Anyone needs their head examined that relies on that lot."

I said that they'd been really helpful when my nan had been in hospital and my granddad (he's dead now) had needed looking after and Mum couldn't manage because of just having had Squirrel.

Paul said that was different. he didn't say how it was different, but I thought that perhaps it was because my nan doesn't live on the Estate. Maybe if people live on the Estate they don't get the same treatment as the rest of society. Or maybe they just don't expect it and therefore they don't ask. You have to be a bit pushy, my nan always says. "Not made of money, are they? Stands to reason. You got to assert yourself. Stick up for your rights."

I couldn't see Paul's mum doing that. I'm sure if she had done, the social services would have been just as helpful to her as they were to my nan. But it wasn't the time to start arguing, so as usual I shut up.

Paul said, "Anyone that relies on *anyone* needs their head examined. You can't trust other folk. You have to look out for yourself in this world."

I said, "You can trust me!" and he said, "Maybe." I said, "You can! You know you can!" and he looked at me, frowning, and said, "Are you going to tell the police where I am?" Of course, I swore I wouldn't, but he kept pushing at me, saying things like, "Suppose they threaten you? Suppose they say you could be had up for obstructing the course of justice?"

I said, "If you're asking me to promise not to tell them, then I'll promise."

Paul just grunted. I could see he didn't trust even me 100 per cent. I was really hurt by that.

I asked him what he was going to do, almost expecting him to say it was none of my business, but he said that he'd thought of a plan. "Only I shall need your help."

His plan was that he was going to take Lily and go off to look for his real dad. It was the first I'd ever heard of Paul's dad, he'd never mentioned him before, but he said he reckoned he knew where to find him all right.

"Up in Liverpool, working on the boats."

I said, "*Liverpool?*" I think I must have looked dismayed, because he said very quickly that as soon as he was settled up there, with his dad, he would ring me. He said Liverpool wasn't that far away and we could still see each other, but my stomach was churning and I could feel my heart thudding and banging, because all I could think was that we wouldn't be together any more.

Paul said, "I'll always love you, Tracey," and Lily looked up and gurgled and said something that sounded like "Lub!" and I tried to laugh but only started to cry, and Paul said urgently that he didn't want to go away but he knew if he stayed they'd just send him and Lily back home and "next time that bast'd'll kill her for sure."

So I tried very hard to be a bit stronger, and reminded myself that if you love someone, if you really and truly love someone, you put their interests before your own, you don't snivel and whine and be self-pitying, at any rate not until later, in private, and I scrubbed at my eyes and said, "OK. What do you want me to do?"

Paul said he wanted me to bring some stuff "tomorrow lunchtime". It was going to mean bunking off school (we're not allowed out in the lunch break), but I didn't mind that. I asked him what sort of stuff, and he said, "We need some other clothes. We need something to change our appearance, 'cause I bet the coppers have a description of what we're wearing."

I said yes, they had; they'd been saying on television how Paul was last seen in his school uniform, grey trousers and red sweater, and how Lily had had on a red jumper and skirt.

"So could you get us something else, d'you think? Anything'd do. Just so long as it makes us look a bit different, else they'll pick us up for sure."

I said that perhaps a pair of Mum's jeans would fit Paul – Mum is tiny, like me, so that even though Paul's only thirteen, he's as tall as she is – and that I could maybe bring along some of Squirrel's stuff for Lily. Squirrel is a weed and Lily is quite a big, chunky child.

"It'd still be a bit large," I said, "but I can't think where else I could get anything."

Paul said that some of Squirrel's stuff would do fine. "Oh, and a pair of scissors," he said. "I'll need a pair of scissors."

I said, "Scissors?" thinking that a knife and spoon or even a tin opener would be of more use. Paul made chopping motions with his fingers.

"Scissors," he said.

I thought he must want them for cutting his hair, which is quite long but not as long as all that. I said, "I don't think that'd make much difference. It's a pity you're not a grown-up or you could wear dark glasses and a false moustache."

Paul said that if he were a grown-up, none of

this would have happened. And he said he still wanted the scissors.

When I got back to the park, Ess was sitting right where I had left her. She had her eyes scrunched tight shut behind her glasses and was mouthing things to herself. (Reciting French verbs, she told me afterwards.) Ess is amazing. I think she really actually *enjoys* learning things.

We walked to the bus stop in a strained sort of silence. I knew that Ess was bursting to know what had happened, and as a matter of fact I was bursting to tell her. It's just that I wasn't sure that I ought. But then I thought, if I couldn't trust Ess, I couldn't trust anyone. And I had to trust somebody. In spite of what Paul said about "having to look out for yourself in this world", I don't think you can go through life without having at least one other person you can confide in. I know I'd promised not to tell the police, but that was different. The police had a job to do. Ess was my *friend*.

So as soon as we were on the bus I came out with it, all about Paul's stepdad getting violent when he was drunk, and his mum being too petrified to say anything, and Paul being convinced that if he went to the police they'd send him back home and then his stepdad would *really* have it in for him.

"And for Lily," I said. "Ess, you should have seen her! She's been beaten black and blue!"

Ess was terribly shocked. I think she was almost more shocked than I was, because at least I'm used to a family that is quite rumbustious (I think that's how you spell it), whereas Ess is an only child and used to peace and quiet. No one ever says so much as a cross word in Ess's family. And they hardly ever watch television, but when they do it's mostly for improving things like current affairs and nature programmes. They don't even like Ess to watch the soaps as they feel they are not "educational". Not that Ess particularly wants to watch soaps. She is a bit of a phenomenon, really; I'm sure she'll end up as one of those professor-type people that live in universities and never see the light of day. She is truly *extraordinary*.

She is also in many ways quite practical. She wanted to know, for instance, when was the last time that Paul had seen his real dad. She said, "Does he keep in touch with him? Does he actually have an address for him?"

I said I didn't know; I hadn't thought to ask.

"Because, I mean, what happens if he turns up on the doorstep with Lily and his dad takes one look and says, 'I don't want her here'? I mean, it's not his responsibility, is it?"

I had to admit that it wasn't. "But he seems to think it'll be all right," I said.

Ess shook her head. "It doesn't sound to me as if he's really thought things out."

I asked Ess what she reckoned he should do, and Ess said at once, "Go to the police." I wailed, "But he doesn't trust them! He's scared they'll send him back!"

Ess agreed that that was a problem. She then came up with the idea of social workers, but I said I'd already suggested that and Paul didn't trust social workers, either.

"He says they're useless."

"Hm." Ess frowned, and rubbed a finger over the bridge of her nose, which is what she does when she is engaged in deep thought processes.

I waited, until in the end she gave a long sigh and said, "If he won't, then we'll have to. Go to the police, I mean."

In a panic I said, "I can't! I promised him!"

"We don't have to tell them where he is," said Ess. "We don't even have to tell them that he rang. But I do think we have to tell them about you-know-what."

I looked at her, uncertainly. What did she mean by you-know-what?

Ess turned her eyes on me, round and solemn behind the thick lenses.

"About us knowing where he was on Saturday night."

I swallowed. This wasn't something I'd had a chance to discuss with Ess. I hadn't realized she'd have thought of it for herself, but of course she had. Ess is brighter than I am, so really and truly she was bound to have done.

"It only occurred to me this evening," she said. "While I was sitting there doing French verbs ... it suddenly struck me: we can give him an alibi."

I nodded, rather glumly. I wasn't looking forward to telling Mum.

"I know we'll get into a row," said Ess, "and you probably more than me, but me as well for telling lies, but we can't let them go on thinking he's guilty."

"No, I know." I'd already come to the same conclusion. I was going to have to be brave. "But I don't see there's any need for you to get involved," I said. Why should Ess have to get into trouble? All she'd been trying to do was help, which was what any friend would do.

"You'll need someone to corroborate," said Ess. (I have just looked this word up.) "Someone to back your story." She's always very tactful about explaining some of the language she uses. She manages to do it without making you feel too desperately inferior. "Otherwise the police'll think you're just saying it because he's your boyfriend."

"I've thought of that," I said. "But it's all right, her-next-door'll do if they want someone else. She was there as usual, spying on us. I don't have to mention your name at all."

I could see that Ess was tempted. She really dreads rows and unpleasantness.

"Well – " she said. And then, shunting at her glasses, "I'll back you up if you need me."

But I was the one who'd got myself into this mess; I didn't see why poor old Ess should have to share any of the blame. I said, "I'll go and see her the minute we get in."

"Her-next-door?"

"Old Nosy Parker," I said. I really *hate* that woman. I knew she'd be glad if she could get me into trouble.

Sure enough, when I rang at the bell and the horrid old bat came to answer it, she leered at me, all full of malice, and said, "And what would you be wanting, miss?"

I loathe it when people call me miss like that. But I was really polite. I said, "I'm very sorry to disturb you. I was just wondering ... last Saturday evening ... whether you happened to notice me seeing someone off at about half-past ten?"

This look of evil triumph spread itself across her face and she hissed, "Yes, I did, and what's more I've already been in to tell your ma about it. They had his picture on the telly again ... I thought I recognized him. So I went straight in and told her. He's a bad lot, that boy. It was about time your ma knew what you was up to."

Hideous old bag. I said, "Paul isn't a bad lot! If he was round with me, he couldn't have done what they said he did, could he?" and I ran off down the passage before she had time to do more than just blink. When I got to our door, I turned and yelled "I was going to tell Mum anyway!"

It was true that I was, but I did wish she hadn't gone and got in ahead of me. It made it look as though I was only doing it because now I had to.

When I came into the flat, Dad was here. He and Mum were watching the telly, but they turned it off when they saw me. Dad said, "Tracey, your mum and I want a word with you."

If I'd had a wax model of old Gossipy Gullick, I'd have stuck pins into it all night through.

Long ones.

chapter **six**

I KNEW I had to get in first. Ever so quickly I said, "Mum! Dad! There's something I've got to tell you ... You know on Saturday, when you went to Auntie Ellen's?"

Mum and Dad shot these glances at each other. Dad said, "Yes?"

I took a deep, deep breath and gabbled, "You know Mum told me I was to be home by seven o'clock and spend the evening with Ess and I said that I would, well I didn't, I spent it here with Paul, and I know that I shouldn't have done, and I'm really, really sorry, but all we did was just watch a video, and it was a nice video, it was one that Ess lent me, it's her favourite, it's *Wuthering Heights*, and, Dad, it's a *classic*, and that's all we did, just watched a video, and then I went upstairs to Ess when Paul had gone."

There was a bit of a silence after I'd spouted all this. I actually expected them to get mad and bawl at me, or at any rate I expected Mum to, because Mum's like me, she tends to get rather aerated, and we do sometimes yell at each other, but as a matter of fact they were really good about it. Both of them. Dad said gravely that he was glad I'd told them "before we had to tackle you about it".

Mum was a bit more reproachful. She said, "I did think we could trust you to keep your promises, Tracey."

Dad said, "Oh, come on, now, Ro!" (Mum's name is Rhoda.) "At least she's come clean. I'd sooner she felt able to talk to us than did things behind our back and never let on." Dad is always softer on me than Mum. Maybe it's because he's out working and doesn't see as much of me.

He said, "So long as she gives us her word she'll never do anything like it again – "

"Won't get the chance," said Mum.

"Mum, I'm sorry," I said. "I am, honestly!"

Mum just grunted. Dad said, "Let's not be too hard on her. It's not the end of the world. And you and I weren't exactly plaster saints, were we? Remember that time we went on holiday together, just the two of us, and told your mam we were going with a group?"

Mum said, "Bob, we were *seventeen*!"

"Yeah, but we never owned up, did we? At least our Tracey's got a conscience."

Needless to say, by this time I was glowing bright scarlet, practically frazzling everything I looked at. I thought maybe I'd better get the whole lot off my chest (but leaving Ess out of it), so I hastily confessed about old Gossipy Gullick, how I'd just been round to see her and how she said she'd already told on me.

"But I was going to tell you anyway, Mum! I swear I was!"

Mum got a bit tight-lipped at this and said, "You honestly expect us to believe you?" Dad was more interested in knowing why I'd done it. Gone next door, I mean. He knows I can't stand that woman (and that she can't stand me). He said, "A bit of a daft thing to do, wasn't it? Going and putting ideas in her head?"

So then I had to explain how I'd suddenly woken up to the fact that I could give Paul an alibi but needed to check that her-next-door could corroborate.

"I had to make sure there was someone who

could back me up," I said, in case Mum and Dad didn't know what corroborate meant. "I had to check, if the police asked her, that she'd say Paul was here."

"Hang about!" said Dad."Hang about! Are you saying that she can give the lad an alibi?"

"She can!" I said. "He was still here with me at half-past ten, so how could he have been at home bashing Lily?"

Slowly, Dad said, "You are quite sure of this, our kid? You're sure you've got your timings right?"

It was Mum who confirmed that I had. She said, "Mrs Gullick told me ... sneaking out like thieves in the night at gone ten-thirty. I should have thought! I just never put two and two together. I was that cross with our Tracey, I just never made the connection."

Dad was all for ringing the police right there and then, but Mum didn't want him to in case they sent a patrol car round and her-next-door happened to catch sight of it.

"Which she most likely would, and then it'd be all round the neighbourhood in next to no time. I can do without that, thank you very much!"

Dad said in that case he'd better get the car out and drive me straight down to the station.

"We can't have them going on accusing the lad of something he didn't do."

"Well, not at the time they claim," said Mum. "Happen the neighbour got it wrong. More like eleven o'clock."

Mum still thought Paul was guilty, in spite of my alibi. I couldn't very well tell her that I'd already been round to the Estate and spoken to Paul's neighbour. If I told her that, she'd know I'd been lying to her again, saying I had to stay on at school. But it didn't matter, the police would be bound to go back and double-check.

"Sounds to me like the lad could be innocent," said Dad.

"So what's he run away for?" Mum wanted to know.

I couldn't tell her that, either; not without letting on I'd seen him.

Dad drove me down to the police station and I had to make an official statement. The police-woman wasn't there – well, another one was, but not WPC Deare. A CID man interviewed me and it was just as well I'd checked with her-next-door, because almost the first thing he said was, "Paul Redwood is your boyfriend. Am I right?"

I knew what he was thinking. I said, "Yes, but I'm not making things up. There's a witness," and I told him about old Gossipy Gullick spying on us through the door crack.

Needless to say, he wanted to know why I hadn't given them this information before. I said that it had only occurred to me this morning, and he said, so why hadn't I gone to my head teacher, and I explained about needing someone to corroborate, "in case you thought I was just trying to clear Paul's name".

The CID man didn't like this. He said that in future it would be wiser if I left the police to do any checking that was necessary. He said, "It's your duty to come straight to us. Withholding vital information could get you into a lot of trouble."

Fortunately he didn't think to ask whether Paul had tried to contact me or whether I'd seen him. If he had, I don't know what I'd have done. I wouldn't have said yes, because of my promise to Paul; but on the other hand, I might have hesitated, owing to being intimidated (when he said get into trouble, what sort of trouble?) and then probably he might not have believed me. He might even have made me take a lie detector test.

Even as it was, he was quite threatening. He kept hinting that if there were things I knew that I wasn't telling them, I could be locked away. He didn't actually *say* I could be locked away, but I knew that was what he wanted me to believe. I kept remembering what Paul had said – "Suppose they threaten you? Suppose they say you could be had up for obstructing the course of justice?" – and I began to think that Paul obviously knew the police better than I did.

I realize they had a job to do, but suddenly I could understand why it was Paul was so terrified they'd take his stepdad's word rather than his and simply send him and Lily straight back home again. By the time they discovered their mistake, it might be too late.

As we left the station, the CID man said, "If he gets in touch, I shall expect you to tell us." Dad got quite huffy about it. He said, "There's no call to go bullying her."

That made me feel *really* guilty, because there was Dad sticking up for me, never dreaming that I was withholding vital information. It made me feel scared, as well. I'd always thought of the police as being jolly and friendly, like Sergeant Rogers that sometimes comes in to school to give us talks on drugs and suchlike. I was discovering that when you cross them they can turn quite nasty.

Of course, it wasn't the CID man's fault; I accept that. I was the one that was obstructing the course of justice. Which I suppose technically makes me a criminal. But he wasn't in the least sympathetic and I didn't trust him one bit. If it had been Sergeant Rogers, I would have trusted him. I might even have been tempted to break my promise, because Sergeant Rogers would have listened. I didn't have the feeling that the CID man would. He'd just have dismissed me as Paul's girlfriend and a stupid kid. So wild horses wouldn't have got me confessing anything to him.

Instead, I did what Paul asked. Next morning, when Dad had left for work and Mum was in the kitchen getting breakfast, and Squirrel was in the kitchen getting under her feet (he's a right mummy's boy is Squirrel: he likes to be wherever Mum is), I crept into Mum and Dad's bedroom and helped myself to a pair of Mum's old jeans and one of her indoor sweaters. She calls them indoor sweaters when they're too washed up to be worn outside. I wouldn't have taken any of her good stuff.

Then I sneaked into Squirrel's room and nicked a pair of his school trousers. They're these horrible grey things with an elasticated waist. I reckoned if Paul cut them short and held them up with safety pins they'd do OK for Lily. I also took an old torn anorak that I didn't think Mum would miss, since it was right at the back of the wardrobe and in any case he'd probably grown out of it.

After that I rushed back to my room and shoved everything into my school bag, which meant leaving out some of my books, which was going to get me into a row. I'd just have to say I'd forgotten them (not that that is ever accepted as an excuse – they still bawl at you). I borrowed the scissors from the bathroom cabinet, and even remembered safety pins, big ones for pinning trousers.

Mum happened to catch sight of my bag as I was leaving for school. She said, "What on earth have you got in there? Half a ton of house bricks?" I pulled a face and said, "Just books."

I hate lying to Mum, but I knew if I'd told her the truth she'd have insisted on me going to the police. She'd have said, "If Paul isn't guilty, then he's got nothing to fear." And if I'd told her about his stepdad, she'd have started on about social workers and how they would take care of things. Mum has great faith in social workers. And in the police. She wouldn't have understood why Paul was terrified. Maybe I wouldn't have done if I hadn't seen what had happened to him and Lily.

I got into *real* trouble at school for not bringing my rotten French book with me. Mr Barker, who is our French teacher, practically accused me of leaving it behind on purpose. He knows I hate French. He's a pig at the best of times, though as a matter of fact pigs are pleasant, intelligent and amiable creatures, exactly the opposite of Mr Barker, so why I call him a pig I really don't know. It's an insult to pigs. Mr Barker is just foul.

At breaktime I was walking round the playground with Carrie when we came across someone's baseball cap that they'd left lying on a bench. As casually as I could, I picked it up and said, "I suppose I'd better take it to lost prop."

Carrie said, "Why bother?" but fortunately she didn't keep on about it – I mean, normally I *wouldn't* have bothered, it wouldn't even have occurred to me – as she was too engrossed in telling me the story of a film she'd seen. The story was so long and so complicated that she hadn't even finished it by the time the bell rang.

I stuffed the cap into my bag alongside Mum's jeans and sweater and Squirrel's trousers and anorak. For a moment I felt like a thief, which actually I suppose I was, but then I thought of poor little Lily and all the terrible black bruises on her body, and I reckoned that if someone's baseball cap was going to help her and Paul get away I was justified in taking it.

Year 8 has late lunch on a Thursday, so it was one o'clock before I could sneak out of school and make a dash for the bus stop. I'd had to tell Carrie I was bunking off, though I didn't tell her where I was going. I said that I was meeting Ess and we were going to look at some kittens. Carrie said I was mad. She said if I got caught I'd be in dead trouble.

I don't know why we're not supposed to leave the premises during the lunch break. It seems a stupid rule to me. Carrie thought perhaps it was something to do with fire regulations.

"They like to know who's in school and who

isn't so they can check there are people still inside being burnt to death."

I said, "Well, if a fire breaks out while I'm gone you'll know I'm OK."

"You won't be OK if someone sees you," said Carrie.

But nobody did see me, either on the way out or the way back. It's quite easy to bunk off, really. With a thousand kids, they can't keep an eye on everyone.

I bought some apples and crisps and a bottle of Coke and headed for Safton Road just as fast as I could. It was a good thing I'd thought of food, because Paul and Lily were starving again. Paul said he hadn't dared go out and buy anything in case he was recognized, especially as he'd have had to take Lily with him. He couldn't risk leaving her on her own, even for just fifteen minutes. In any case, he needed what little money he had for getting them to Liverpool.

He was pleased with the stuff I'd brought him, and in particular with the baseball cap. He said he could wear it with the peak pulled down over his eyes. I had to hurry to get back in time for afternoon school before anyone noticed I was missing, so I couldn't stay to see how Lily looked in Squirrel's trousers and anorak. Paul said he was going to try and make a dash for it later on that day, at about five-thirty, when lots of people would be heading home from work, so that he and Lily could lose themselves in the crowd.

I said, "You'll need more food." I told him I would come again after school and bring him some. "I can borrow some money from Carrie. She won't mind."

Paul told me I'd already done more than enough and that I shouldn't bother, he and Lily would manage somehow, but I couldn't bear the thought of them making the long journey to Liverpool with nothing to eat. I said, "I'll get some chocolate," remembering how Lily had fallen on the Maltesers.

I didn't have a chance to ask him all those questions that Ess had asked, such as did he have an actual address for his dad and did his dad know about Lily. We just kissed each other goodbye and I went haring off up the road to the bus stop, arriving back at school about two seconds before the bell.

"So the place didn't burn down in my absence?" I said to Carrie.

She said, "No, worse luck. How were the kittens?"

I'd forgotten I was supposed to be looking at kittens. I said, "Oh! Lovely."

"What colour are they?"

"Um – tortoiseshell," I said.

"All of them?"

Recklessly I said yes, all of them. Carrie said, "How many were there?" I said, "Six." Carrie said, "*Six?* All tortoiseshell?" She said that was extremely unusual, she'd never heard of that before, and before I could stop her she'd started wittering on all about tortoiseshell cats. How was I to know she was a cat freak? All she's got is one dead ordinary black and white job that they call Moggie, just by way of being original. Actually Mogs is a really nice cat, though not much to look at.

"I'd adore a tortoiseshell," said Carrie.

I took fright at this and immediately said that all the kittens had been spoken for, and Carrie said, "Yes, I *bet*. Six tortoiseshell!"

It wasn't till the afternoon break that I was able to ask her if she could lend me any money. Carrie is such an obliging soul! She handed over £2 just like that. She didn't even ask what I wanted it for.

As soon as school was over I went charging off again to the bus stop, only stopping to spend Carrie's £2 on a supply of chocolate and apples and cartons of milk, which I thought was a reasonably balanced diet and would keep them going until they got to Liverpool (though I had to eat one of the bars of chocolate myself, being in a state of near collapse through having missed lunch).

The bus came within seconds and I was racing up Safton Road by ten-past four, which wasn't bad going. I reached the house, squeezed through the gate, down the side passage and into the back garden. There I had the most terrible shock: the air-raid shelter was empty. Paul and Lily had disappeared.

My immediate panic-stricken thought was that somehow or other the police had managed to find them and I wondered if it was my fault. If perhaps I'd been followed and hadn't realized it. And then, on the floor of the shelter, I saw these twigs arranged in the shape of an arrow. They had quite definitely been arranged; they hadn't just fallen into an arrow shape by accident.

I looked in the direction the arrow was pointing. There was an upturned bucket, and when I moved it I found a note underneath. It had been written on the inside of a wrapper from a bar of KitKat. It was from Paul. It said, "Got scared. Gone to Liverpool. I love you. XXX Paul."

I felt really peculiar, just for a moment. All cold and clammy inside. I was glad that he had got away – oh, I was! Of course. I was! – but all the same I couldn't help feeling hurt that he hadn't stopped to say a proper goodbye. Surely he could just have waited till I came?

On the other hand, I could see that the longer he and Lily stayed in Birmingham, the more chance there was of their being discovered. And he *had* left me a note, which he needn't have done. I mean, it was taking a risk, leaving it in the shelter where anyone could find it. If the police had followed me and seen me looking under the bucket –

The thought so alarmed me that I sprang round, fully expecting to see the CID man, but no one was there, so I destroyed the arrow and put the note away in my bag. I should have destroyed the note as well, probably, but it was all I had left of Paul and I couldn't bring myself to do so.

As I turned to go, I saw something glinting

on the path – a golden strand, gleaming in the sunshine. I bent to pick it up, and it was then that I knew what Paul had wanted the scissors for. He had used them to chop Lily's hair. Her beautiful blonde hair! I pictured the poor little kid, with her big moon face and tiny piggy eyes, all done up in Squirrel's cut-down trousers and his old torn anorak several sizes too big for her, and her lovely hair hacked off short with the bathroom scissors. I knew that the most important thing was for her and Paul to get away before the police could find them and send them back home; I also knew that Lily probably didn't mind about losing her hair. So long as she was with Paul and had plenty of Maltesers and KitKats to eat, the chances were she would be perfectly happy. All the same, it upset me.

I got home and watched some television in a rather miserable silence. Squirrel was in one of his whiny moods, demanding attention and grizzling if he didn't get it. He kept running a toy car up the arm of my chair and along the back of it and down the other side, and then across my lap, all the time making these irritating "vrrm vrrm" noises in my ear until I thought I'd scream if he didn't stop, so I slapped him (but not hard) and told him to pack it in. Of course, he instantly started bawling and Mum took his side as usual and told me not to be so unkind.

"Poor little mite! He's only playing."

I said I didn't see why he had to play over me when there were plenty of other chairs in the room, and Mum said it was because he wanted me to join in. I thought that, as far as I was concerned, he could go on wanting. If Paul had been there, Paul would have played with him; but Paul wasn't there and might never be again. This made *me* feel like bawling, so I suddenly sprang up and said, "I'm going to see Ess!"

I pounded up the stairs and banged on Ess's door, thinking that we could go into her room and have a heart-to-heart, and that Ess would be sympathetic, as she always is, and probably find something to say to cheer me up, but it was her mum who came to the door. She said, "I'm sorry, Esther can't speak to you just now, Tracey. She and I are having a little talk." With that, she practically slammed the door in my face.

I didn't know what to make of it. Ess's mum is a really friendly person as a rule. What on earth could Ess have done to upset her? Ess isn't the sort to do things.

I trailed back downstairs and found Squirrel curled up on the sofa next to Mum, watching the telly and sucking at his thumb as if it were a lollipop. He gave me a look of mingled triumph and reproach, which with immense dignity I ignored.

Dad came in and we had tea and watched the six o'clock news, but there wasn't any mention of Paul and Lily. We'd just finished eating when there was a ring at the door and Mum went to answer it. She came back followed by Ess, looking tearful, and Ess's mum, looking grim. I tried to exchange glances with Ess but she wouldn't. She just wouldn't look at me. I soon understood why.

Mum said, "Tracey, it seems you have some explaining to do."

"About what?" I said, and again I looked at Ess, and again she turned her eyes away from me.

"About going to see Paul and not telling us," said Mum.

chapter **seven**

CATASTROPHE! Ess's mum had gone to take some money out of her housekeeping purse and discovered that £20 was missing ...

It hadn't occurred to her that Ess might have taken it. Ess doesn't do things like that. Her first thought, she said, was that Ess's dad must have borrowed it and forgotten to tell her. But when Ess came back from school she happened to mention it to her – Ess's mum, I mean – and Ess, being Ess, instantly confessed.

I suppose in all fairness there was nothing much else she could do, especially as she'd already been to the building society and had the money all ready in her purse, just waiting to be put back. What I couldn't understand was why she had to go and blab about what she'd taken it for. She didn't have to tell her mum about Paul!

She could just as easily have made something up, like –

Oh, I don't know! Maybe she couldn't. Maybe it's not that easy to make things up on the spur of the moment. Ess isn't a natural-born liar, she's good and gentle and law-abiding and I shouldn't have got mad at her. I sent her this look like daggers across the room, and for the first time she met my gaze. Her lower lip was trembling and her eyes behind her glasses were all swimmy and pathetic and full of desperate apology, and I felt like your actual number-one louse and wanted to go rushing over and hug her and tell her she was forgiven. Poor old Ess! She's not cut out for a life of crime.

I think that I am made of slightly sterner stuff, but even I got the wobbles when Dad said, "Right!" with his mouth all pursed into a grim straight line. "It's back to the cop shop for you, my girl!"

Dad was absolutely furious. I guess he thought I'd made a fool of him, letting him stick up for me in front of the CID man the day before, while knowing the whole time that I was withholding information. He lectured me all the way to the police station and said it would serve me right if they locked me up. I knew they wouldn't really, because I don't think they do if you're only thirteen years old and haven't got a criminal record, but still I had these visions of being put on probation or sent away somewhere.

The same CID man came to interview me. He was all squat and tubby, with a huge potbelly and hands that looked like footballs with pork sausages growing out of them. His breath smelt of cigarettes and booze. He kept putting his face close to mine and I got the fumes all over me. Ugh! Pollution.

I had to tell him about Paul; I didn't have any choice now that Ess had gone and spilled the beans. The first thing he wanted to know was the number of the house in Safton Road. I said I couldn't remember, I'd never bothered looking at it, and his face went all enraged and contorted, and I thought that if I'd been a boy he'd have picked me up and shaken me. So very hastily I described the place to him, and he relaxed a bit and said were Paul and Lily still there?

I didn't know what to say to this. I mumbled that they might be or they might not be, and he snarled, "What's that supposed to mean, they might be or they might not be? What the hell's that supposed to mean? Are they or aren't they? When did you last see them?"

I said that I'd last seen them at lunchtime earlier in the day, which was true. He didn't ask me when I'd last been there, so I didn't tell him about going again after school.

He said, "So what makes you think they might not still be there?" and I realized then that the police aren't stupid. I was the one who was stupid, saying they might be or they might not be. While I was hesitating, and wondering what to answer, he roared at me and pounded on the table. "Now, you just listen," he bawled, "and listen well . . . there's a child's life at stake here!"

I'd got the shivers by now because I was really frightened. I mean, there was this policewoman in the room with us, so I knew he wouldn't fly at me or do anything violent, but it was still scary. I knew I had to explain *why* Paul had run away, and why I'd helped him and not gone to the police, so I told him what Paul had said about his stepdad and how he was terrified that Lily would be sent back to him again and how next time he might end up killing her.

Old Sausage Fingers snapped, "It would have made a bit more sense if you'd told us this immediately!" but at least he didn't sound quite so manic any more. He assured me that on no account would Lily be sent back until the social services had had a chance to check things out. He also said that while he accepted that I'd acted from the best of motives, I had in fact been extremely silly and irresponsible, because surely I must realize that a thirteen-year-old boy and a handicapped three-year-old "out there on their own, with nowhere to go and no one to turn to" were at grave risk?

I hung my head and said yes, while at the same time thinking that Paul did have someone to turn to, he had his dad up in Liverpool. But that was something I couldn't tell them even now, because of my promise.

He still didn't let it drop, old Big Gut, that question of why I thought Paul and Lily might not be at Safton Road any more.

"Did he have plans? Was he going to take her somewhere? Now, come on, Tracey, for goodness' sake! We've got to find those kids before something happens to them. Just bear in mind that you'll be responsible if anything does. *Where was he going to take her?*"

I closed my eyes and said, "London."

"London? What was he going to do in London?"

"Find his dad," I said. "His real dad."

He obviously believed me, because he left me with the policewoman and went crashing out of the room, yelling at someone I couldn't see. I supposed he was going to go to New Street and check if anyone answering Paul's description had bought tickets for London. I still felt scared, but at least I hadn't given Paul away. I hadn't broken my promise. By now he and Lily would be on their way to Liverpool. How long did it take to get to Liverpool? I didn't know, but it couldn't be that long. I might even have a phone call later that night and it would be Paul letting me know that he and Lily were safe, with his dad. The police would be so relieved that maybe they'd forget I'd said London, though I could always pretend that London was what Paul had told me.

It shows how easy it would be to drift into a life of crime. Once you start telling lies it seems there is no way of stopping. Ess swears she'll never tell another one as long as she lives. She says it is too nerve-racking and you only get found out in the end. She is probably right, she usually is. But what do you do if you love someone and they swear you to secrecy? It was a question I really needed to ask, but there was no way I could have asked Mum or Dad; not that night. The minute I got home, Mum started on at me. She was bitterly disappointed, she said. "You've upset me, Tracey! You've let us down."

She really knows how to make you feel rough, though I guess I deserved it. Even when I told her about Paul's stepdad, which I thought would side-track her, because she hates cruelty to children – it's one of the things that really gets her going – all she did was wail, "That was even more reason for you to go to the police!"

I think what upset her more than anything was the fact that I'd told so many lies. It made me feel a bit queasy, wondering what she was going to say when Paul rang up from Liverpool. "I thought you said he'd gone to London!" And then I'd have to lie all over again and say that that was what Paul had told me. Oh, Ess is right! I know she is. I swore to myself then that I would never *ever* lie to Mum again. Not ever.

As it happened, I didn't have to because I never got a telephone call from Liverpool. Instead, on the nine o'clock news, they announced that "Birmingham run-away Paul Redwood and his three-year-old half-sister, Lily" had been picked up earlier that evening by the police at Euston Station.

In London.

Mum said, "Thank goodness for that! At least you got something right."

Me, I just couldn't believe it. I still had Paul's note in my school bag. I read it again when I went to bed that night. "Gone to Liverpool," that was what it said. So how come they'd picked him up in London?

Because I'd told them London, that was how. I hadn't meant to shop him, but that was what I'd done. I didn't think that he would ever forgive me.

I didn't see Ess over the weekend. I was scared to go up to her place in case her mum had forbidden her to be friends with me any more. She was scared (she told me later) that I wouldn't *want* to be friends any more. So I stayed in and played with Squirrel, hoping this would make Mum relent towards me, and Ess (she told me this later) read a book called *War and Peace*, which is about 1,000 pages long and which she'd been meaning to read for ages. She enjoyed it, she said – "Except when I was worrying about you and me and whether we were friends any more."

I wish I could say that I'd enjoyed playing with Squirrel, but he's such a rotten loser, he always starts blubbing and saying that I've cheated. (As if I'd bother!) And it didn't make Mum relent. She just said she was surprised I couldn't make allowances for such a little chap and let him win, just now and again.

I said, "He can't win all the time, life isn't like that." Mum snapped, "Just make *allowances*."

On Sunday we went to our nan's, in King's Norton. Of course, Nan had heard about everything; Mum must have been on the telephone. She said, "Oh, dear, our Tracey! I hear you're in disgrace. Why don't you come and tell your old nan all about it?" and she took me into the front room and closed the door on nosy parkers (Uncle Jim and Auntie Betty were there and they are *real* gluttons for gossip, almost as bad as her-next-door).

So I poured everything out and Nan listened and nodded and heard me right through to the end before speaking, and when she did speak it wasn't to tick me off.

She said, "Love's a wonderful thing, our Tracey, no doubt about it, but it can get you into all kinds of trouble."

I said, "But what can you do? If someone swears you to secrecy?"

Nan said that really and truly, if he loved me, Paul shouldn't have done that. She said, "It was putting too great a burden on you. It was too much to ask."

"But I was the only one he could trust!" I said, and Nan agreed that it was difficult.

"Things are rarely clear cut. We all have to make up our minds what's right and what's wrong." She said that she didn't think what I had done was wrong, "just misguided". "The only wrong thing you did was to cheat on your mam right at the beginning, but I don't expect you need me to tell you that."

Very humbly I said that I didn't, though I couldn't help reflecting that if Paul hadn't been with me that evening the police would still think he was the one who had bashed Lily, and there wouldn't be any way of proving otherwise, so that was a case of good coming out of evil – well, no, not evil, exactly. Not even Mum accused me of being *evil*. But it's certainly a case of a bad thing leading to a good one, and that is a bit of a moral puzzle, I think.

I wish I could discuss it with Ess, but she is

still away unfortunately. At least before she went we were able to have a bit of a talk, so that we know we are still friends. I don't think I could bear it if we weren't.

It's half-term now, which is how I've been able to do all this writing. I hoped that if I wrote everything down it might help me to feel a bit happier but in fact it seems to have had just the opposite effect. I am feeling utterly miserable. The main thing that's making me miserable is the fear that Paul is going to hate me for breaking my promise. I know I told them London, thinking he had gone to Liverpool, but if I had just kept quiet he would never have been picked up.

The policewoman came round to talk to me. The one that was there right at the beginning, with Mr Smethurst. She was quite nice. She told me that Paul couldn't possibly have been going to London (or Liverpool or *anywhere*) to find his real dad as his real dad was dead. He had been killed in what she called "a drunken brawl" when Paul was a baby, and Paul knew this. He had just been spinning me a yarn. She said he had probably done it with good intentions, to stop me worrying.

She also said that although he and Lily were

back in Birmingham, they hadn't been sent back to Paul's mum and stepdad. They had been taken into care, which meant being in a children's home, and Lily at least would probably be fostered for a while, until, as she put it, "things were sorted out".

I am sure that Paul must hate being in a children's home. I would hate it myself. But I think that Paul probably hates it even more than most people. I remember once he said to me, "They're like prisons, them places. You wouldn't get me in one!"

I wonder if even then he had a fear that that was where he might end up? Like if ever the social services had discovered what was happening to him and Lily and took them away from home. I would just die, I would just shrivel and *die*, if anyone took me away from Mum and Dad.

The policewoman thinks that Paul will probably be staying on at school. That means he will be there on Monday. I ought to be excited and looking forward to it, because only a short while ago I was convinced we would never see each other again, but in fact I am dreading it in case he refuses to talk to me. He trusted me and I let him down!

Ess is coming home tomorrow. I wonder if she will be allowed to come and see me?

She was! We sat in my room and had this really long talk. First of all, she said she was sorry for giving the game away to her mum, but I told her there wasn't anything else she could have done and that I would probably have done the same in her place. I said, "It's not easy to suddenly think of a reason why you'd have needed £20." Ess said, "No, and I felt bad enough as it was, taking her housekeeping money."

She then wanted to know what had happened about Paul, and I told her what the policewoman had told me, about him being back in Birmingham and being in care. She seemed to think that that was a good thing, because at least it would mean he and Lily weren't being abused any more, but she did agree that it was a horrible situation. I said, "Yes, and I'm the one who's to blame for it."

Ess said hotly that I most certainly was *not*. She said Paul's stepdad was to blame if anyone was. "And his mum, too, for letting it happen and not doing anything to stop it." She also said that if Paul's real dad was dead (A drunken brawl! It sounds so awful), then it was just as well the police had picked up him and Lily, because however could they have survived in London?

"Terrible things happen to kids in London. There are these disgusting people who hang about railway stations waiting to meet them off trains, then they take them away and make them – " here she lowered her voice – "make them be prostitutes."

I couldn't imagine anyone making Paul be anything he didn't want to be – he fights like a tiger when he's angry – but I had to admit that Ess was right about London. You're always reading stories in the papers about the dreadful things that happen down there. On the other hand, that still didn't stop me feeling that I'd betrayed him.

I said this to Ess and she considered me, very gravely and with a solemn frown, as if wondering whether to say something or whether to keep quiet, until in the end I couldn't bear it any longer and said, "What are you thinking?"

"I was thinking," said Ess, "that I don't know how you can say what you just said ... about betraying him."

"He trusted me!" I said. "He trusted me and I let him down!"

"But he didn't trust you," said Ess. "That's the whole point."

I stared at her. Very slowly, I said, "What do you mean, he didn't trust me?"

"Well, he didn't," said Ess, "did he? That note he left you – " Needless to say, I'd shown it to her. "Why's he say he's gone to Liverpool?"

"To put people off the scent!"

"What people? *You?*"

"The police!"

"So he wrote the note for the police?"

"Well – yes. Sort of. In case they – they might have followed me."

"I see." Ess nodded. "So you were just a kind of fall guy?"

I don't know where Ess learns these expressions, considering she almost never watches television.

"He didn't tell you the truth," said Ess, "did he?"

"Well – n-no." He had quite definitely told me he was going to Liverpool. He had said that was where his real dad was.

"So he wasn't trusting you! He was scared you might talk."

"Yes, and he was right, 'cause I did." I said it glumly. "If I hadn't told them he'd gone to London they'd never have found him."

"Look." Ess spoke kindly, patiently, as if spelling things out to a child. "First of all, it's just as well they found him. We both agree on that."

"Yes," I bleated, "but I bet Paul wouldn't. He'll hate it in a children's home!"

"It's still better than being in London." Ess knows how to stick to her guns. She can be stubborn when she wants. "That's point number one." (She is also very orderly.) "Point number two, if he had *really* trusted you, he'd have told you the truth. He'd have told you London. Then you'd have told the police Liverpool – or Manchester, or Swansea, or just whatever occurred to you. And then he wouldn't have been picked up. So it's totally his own fault, 'cause if he'd've trusted you it wouldn't have happened. So there!"

There was a silence, while I digested this new view of things. Ess was right, of course (when isn't she?). I remembered Paul telling me how you had to look out for yourself in this world, how you couldn't afford to trust anyone. And he *hadn't* trusted me. He'd fed me a deliberate lie because he was so sure that I'd break under pressure. He thought my promise would go for nothing.

"If you ask me," said Ess, "you're the one ought to be feeling betrayed, not him."

Again, she is probably right; only I can't see it that way. If Paul had been running for his life, then I think he *would* have trusted me. But he was running for Lily's life and he couldn't afford to trust anyone. I don't feel that he betrayed me, but I still have this terrible cold fear in the pit of my stomach that *he* is going to feel that I have betrayed *him*.

He hasn't telephoned me, which surely he would have done if he still loved me?

Mum has started to mellow a bit now that she has had a chance to think things over. She said to me today, "That poor young lad! What he must have gone through." She accepts, now, that it was his stepdad that was doing all the bashing. I asked her what was likely to happen to Paul and Lily, and she said if there was any justice his stepdad would be locked away so that they could go back and live with their mum. But then she added, rather darkly, "Unless they go soft on him and just give him a caution."

"You mean, not send him to prison?" I said.

Mum shrugged. "There've been cases ... keeping the family together, they call it. Under supervision."

I whispered, "What does that mean?"

"Means they'd be sent back with him still there and the social services would keep an eye on them."

It was plain from the way Mum said it, it wasn't what she would do. Mum reckons anyone beats a kid should be locked up.

I was having that deep, cold feeling in my stomach again.

"It's what Paul was frightened of ... that they'd send him back."

"Well, mebbe they won't," said Mum. "Not if they've any sense. But I'll tell you what, our Trace, if the lad's still in care, we'll have to see about having him round here for a bit of normal family life now and again. You tell him that. When you see him, you tell him. All right?"

I said that I would, but I just don't know whether he'll ever want to talk to me again.

chapter **eight**

OH! ALL my worries have been for nothing! When two people truly love each other, that love cannot so easily be destroyed. How could I ever have doubted?

I was really nervous when I arrived at school, especially as people kept coming up to me and asking me all these questions that I couldn't answer, such as where was Paul? where was he living? what had happened to Lily? etc. Even Carrie was surprised that I hadn't heard from him.

"I'd have thought you'd be the first person he'd ring!"

I muttered that if he was in care then he probably wasn't allowed to make telephone calls, but I could see Carrie was puzzled. After all, being in care isn't like being in prison. Nobody thought that Paul had done anything wrong; not now they knew about his stepdad, which they did, because it had been in the papers.

POLICE TO INTERVIEW RUN-AWAY'S STEPDAD

STEPDAD DID IT, SAYS RUN-AWAY PAUL

Most of the kids seemed to think he was a hero. Some of them thought he should have gone to the police, or maybe told one of the teachers, but there were lots who agreed with Paul that you couldn't trust anyone in authority. Clive Meldrum, whose teeth Paul had once knocked out because Clive had jeered at him for coming from the Estate, actually said what Paul himself had said: "Gorra fend for yourself in this life."

It made me feel quite stupid and inadequate, because I wouldn't have the faintest idea how to fend for myself. I could never have done what Paul did. I mean, just suppose Dad started bashing Squirrel, which in fact is absurd, because Squirrel is the most spoilt child I know, but just suppose he did, and suppose for some reason Mum wasn't there (I am not going to say suppose she was dead, because the very thought terrifies me), I *still* couldn't do what Paul did.

But then, I wouldn't have any need. I've got people I can turn to. Nan, and Ess's mum, and even some of my aunties and uncles. Not all of them, because some of them are daft as brushes; but Auntie Ellen and Uncle Jack, for example. I could go to them. Paul doesn't have anyone.

So anyway, by nine o'clock he still wasn't in school and I was beginning to have another worry, that he wasn't going to come. Then Miss Tench called us all together, all of our year, and said she wanted to talk to us about Paul.

She told us that what he had done he had done for the sake of his little sister; that it may have been mistaken, but he had done it with the best of intentions. She said that he was temporarily in care, which meant he was living in a children's home, while matters were sorted out. Lily was with foster parents. (I was so relieved to hear this! I think if they had tried sending her and Paul back home, Paul would have done something truly terrible.)

Miss Tench said she was telling us all this to satisfy our natural curiosity and concern, but that having told us she didn't want us pestering Paul or nagging at him with questions.

"He's had more than enough to put up with.

Just treat him perfectly normally, the same as you were doing before any of this happened."

Paul turned up just in time for our first class, which was a double period of maths. He didn't look at me, he didn't look at anyone, simply took a seat in the front row and kept his head down.

When it came to the break, I didn't know what to do. I didn't know whether to do what we usually do, which is slink off to one of our secret meeting places, or whether to stick around with Carrie. Carrie was uncertain, too. She said, "Are you going to – " and she wafted her hand – "or shall I stay around?"

Carrie is so loyal! If I'd asked her to stay around, she would have done. Out of the corner of my eye, I saw Paul leaving the classroom. I knew everyone was watching us to see if we were still an item. So I said to Carrie, "I'll see you after the break," and went dashing off to do the rounds of our secret places.

He was waiting for me in the small basement area behind the kitchens, where no one else ever goes as it is not very *salubrious* (a word I learned from Ess), being frequently flooded and smelling of old stale cabbage and cat pee. But at least it is private.

To begin with we were really awkward. I said, "Hi," but Paul just nodded, very curt and formal. So then I said, "How's Lily?" He said, "Lil's fine. She's gone to stay with this family. They're making a right fuss of her."

I said, "What about you?" Paul said he was OK. The home wasn't too bad.

"At least they give you a real proper breakfast."

Then there was a long pause while I searched frantically for something else to say.

"If they hadn't – picked you up – " I said it carefully, choosing my words – "If the police hadn't – found you – "

Quick as a flash Paul said, "We'd still be out there."

"But what would you have done?" I wailed.

"Who knows?" He humped a shoulder. "Kipped down. Gone on the streets. There's lots you can do."

"In summer," I said. "It's all right so long as it's summer!"

"Well, it is summer," said Paul, "isn't it?"

I pointed out that summer didn't last for ever. "What happens when it's cold and wet?"

Paul said, "You tell me."

"When there's snow on the ground and it's raining … it wouldn't be much fun then!"

Paul said, "Not much fun any time, really. But then life isn't, is it? For some people? We can't all lead nice protected lives."

He didn't actually *say* "with loving parents in a council show block", but I knew that was what he meant. Desperately I burst out, "Paul, I'm sorry! I really am sorry!"

His face didn't change. "For what?" he said.

"For what I did!"

He said, "What was that?"

I hung my head. "I told the police," I mumbled.

I didn't want to explain how Ess had already spilt the beans about me going to meet him; I didn't think that would be fair on her. She oughtn't ever to have been involved.

Paul said, "What'd you tell 'em?"

"Told them you'd gone to London."

"What'd you tell 'em that for?"

"'Cause I thought you'd gone to Liverpool!"

It came out as a sort of self-pitying whinge. Paul studied me for a bit, then quite coldly turned away.

"I knew I shouldn't have trusted you," he said.

It was over. It was finished. All my worst nightmares had come true.

"Paul!" I caught at his sleeve. He swung back.

"What?"

There was that look in his eyes that I recognized. That look that said, "Just keep away from me. No more questions! OK?"

Quite suddenly, something inside me went *twang*. Like something snapping. Something breaking. If I'd believed in violence, I might have hit him. But I don't, so I didn't. Instead, I put my face right close up to his and in this ice-cold voice which I almost couldn't believe was coming from me, I hissed, "If you'd told me the truth, you'd still be free! I lied for you, because I thought you trusted me!"

"I told you," he muttered, "I don't trust anyone."

"Well, it's about time you learned!" I snarled. And I spun round on my heel and began walking back, very quickly, towards school.

To be honest with you, I was hoping – I was *praying* – that he'd come after me. All I wanted was for him to say he was sorry. And that he still loved me. But he didn't.

I was on my own as I reached the school

entrance. I was on my own as I walked up the corridor. I was still on my own as I collected my books and headed off for the next lesson, which was French with Mr Barker.

We couldn't have sat together in French even if Paul had wanted because he has this thing, Mr Barker does, about keeping the sexes separate. One time Clive Meldrum yelled, "What if we're bi, sir? Where do we sit then?" and got told off for being insolent.

So I sat near the back on one side of the gangway and Paul sat two seats away on the other. He didn't look at me, he might not even have known that I was there; but half-way through the class, while Mr Barker's mouthing off about past participles or some such, Paul suddenly leans backwards, tilts his chair, reaches across the gangway and drops this note on to Myra Carmirelli's desk. Myra picks it up, disdainfully, between finger and thumb, as if it's something unspeakable, such as a dead cockroach. Slowly, with one eye on Mr Barker, she turns and deposits the note in front of me.

Carrie saw her do it, and so did several others, but I didn't think Mr Barker had. I opened it and read:

F oxglove	M ichael
O range	E dward
R oger	
G ordon	
I vor	
V ictor	
E dward	

I vor	L ima	Y ellow
	O range	O range
	V ictor	U ncle
	E dward	

That was when I knew that everything was going to be all right.

Unfortunately Mr Barker has eyes all over his head and demanded to see what I was looking at and check whether it had anything to do with the past participle. Feeling cheeky, I said, "No, sir, it's all in the present tense, sir," and he snarled at me, "Don't come any of that smart-mouth stuff with me, Tracey Blair!" but I didn't give two straws.

So then he made me go out front and tear the note up and drop it in the waste bin, where I just knew someone like Clive Meldrum was going to go rooting as soon as class was over. But I didn't give two straws for Clive Meldrum, either.

As I walked back up the gangway, Paul sent me this agonized glance. Silently, I mouthed back the message: 'Ivor Lima Orange . . .'

True love really *is* for ever.

compiled by LEXUS *with Wendy Morris*

German consultant
Dagmar Förtsch

FAST A-Z REFERENCE GRAMMAR FOR EXAMS AND SELF STUDY

Chambers

British Library Cataloguing in Publication Data

A catalogue record for this book is
available from the British Library

ISBN 0-550-22061-5

Cover illustration by Michael Dancer
Cover design by Grafik Design Works

Printed and bound in Great Britain by Cox & Wyman Ltd